Antonia Clare   JJ Wilson

D0363303

INTERMEDIATE

Total English

Workbook (with key)

Longman

Contents

1 Friends

LESSON 1.1 (p4–5)
Vocabulary: verbs, adjectives, prepositions
Grammar: auxiliary verbs
Pronunciation: numbers
Reading: Shenzen, China

LESSON 1.2 (p6–7)
Vocabulary: computers
Grammar: Present Simple vs Present Continuous
Writing: an email
Listening: email relationships

LESSON 1.3 (p8–9)
Grammar: Present Perfect vs Past Simple
Vocabulary: *for* and *since*
Pronunciation: /æ/ or /ə/?
Reading: Brotherly love?

Review and consolidation unit 1 (p10–11)

2 Media

LESSON 2.1 (p12–13)
Vocabulary: newspapers
Grammar: passive
How to: give opinions, agree and disagree
Reading: The Latest News

LESSON 2.2 (p14–15)
Vocabulary: TV programmes
How to: deal with problems
Grammar: *who, whose, which, where*
Reading: When no news is real news

LESSON 2.3 (p16–17)
Vocabulary: regular and irregular verbs
Pronunciation: verb endings
Grammar: Past Simple and Past Continuous
Listening: news headlines

Review and consolidation unit 2 (p18–19)

3 Lifestyle

LESSON 3.1 (p20–21)
Vocabulary: home
Grammar: Present Continuous vs *going to/will* for future
Writing: a formal letter
Reading: House swap with a difference
Listening: House swap

LESSON 3.2 (p22–23)
Vocabulary: adjectives for describing place
Grammar: comparatives/superlatives
Reading: Think your city is best?

LESSON 3.3 (p24–25)
Vocabulary: compound nouns
Pronunciation: compound nouns
Grammar: future probability
Formal phone calls
Reading: 2020 – how technology will rule our lives

Review and consolidation unit 3 (p26–27)

4 Wealth

LESSON 4.1 (p28–29)
Vocabulary: time and money collocations; phrasal verbs
Grammar: question tags
Listening: financial crime

LESSON 4.2 (p30–31)
Vocabulary: personal qualities
Grammar: modal verbs
Writing: an invitation and response
Pronunciation: stressed syllables
Reading: How not to get rich quick

LESSON 4.3 (p32–33)
Vocabulary: opposites
Pronunciation: word stress
Grammar: *if/when/unless/as soon as* with first conditional
Reading: RFID

Review and consolidation unit 4 (p34–35)

5 Spare time

LESSON 5.1 (p36–37)
Vocabulary: free time activities
Grammar: Present Perfect Simple vs Continuous
Pronunciation: contractions
How to: correct response
Reading and listening: The genius

LESSON 5.2 (p38–39)
Vocabulary: books and films
Pronunciation: /æ/ /e/ /ɑː/ sounds
Grammar: gerunds vs infinitives
How to: describe a film or book
Listening: four conversations

LESSON 5.3 (p40–41)
Vocabulary: food and eating out
Writing: a summary
Grammar: countable vs uncountable
How to: recommend a restaurant
Reading: a restaurant review

Review and consolidation unit 5 (p42–43)

6 Holidays

LESSON 6.1 (p44–45)
Vocabulary: travel
Reading: Past Perfect
Grammar: Past Perfect vs Past Simple
How to: describe a photo
Listening: collocations

LESSON 6.2 (p46–47)
Vocabulary: places to visit in a city
Pronunciation: how to sound polite
How to: get around a new place
Grammar: uses of *like*
Writing: a quick guide
Reading: Out and about on Planet Earth

LESSON 6.3 (p48–49)
Vocabulary: adjectives to describe natural places
Grammar: articles
Pronunciation: interest and surprise
How to: show interest and surprise
Reading: Travel agents' true stories

Review and consolidation unit 6 (p50–51)

7 Education

LESSON 7.1 (p52–53)
Vocabulary: education
Grammar: subject and object questions
Reading: Learning from mistakes

LESSON 7.2 (p54–55)
Vocabulary: adjectives
Grammar: *used to/would*
Listening: childhood
Pronunciation: silent letters

LESSON 7.3 (p56–57)
Vocabulary: old age
Grammar: *could/was able to/managed to* for past ability
Reading: retirement

Review and consolidation unit 7 (p58–59)

8 Change

LESSON 8.1 (p60–61)
Vocabulary: phrases with *change*
Reading and vocabulary: the law
Grammar: second conditional

LESSON 8.2 (p62–63)
Vocabulary: global issues
How to: talk about change
Grammar: adverbs
Listening: a voluntary worker describes his work

LESSON 8.3 (p64–65)
Vocabulary: life decisions
Grammar: third conditional
Listening: decisions

Review and consolidation unit 8 (p66–67)

9 Jobs

LESSON 9.1 (p68–69)
Vocabulary: work
Grammar: *make, let, allow*
Listening: casual Fridays

LESSON 9.2 (p70–71)
Vocabulary: *-ing/-ed* adjectives
Grammar: reported speech
Reading: The boss from hell?

LESSON 9.3 (p72–73)
Grammar: past obligation/permission
Vocabulary: advertisements
Reading: Realise your dream …

Review and consolidation unit 9 (p74–75)

10 Memories

LESSON 10.1 (p76–77)
Vocabulary: verbs connected with memory
Grammar: *wish/if only*
Vocabulary: nature collocations
Reading: a 'brain pill'

LESSON 10.2 (p78–79)
Vocabulary: describing great people
Grammar: past tenses review
How to: say numbers

LESSON 10.3 (p80–81)
Grammar: phrasal verbs
Writing: formal vs informal
Listening: how to remember

Review and consolidation unit 10 (p82–83)

Answer key (p84–94)

1.1 Friends

Vocabulary | verbs, adjectives, prepositions

1 Complete the sentences with words and phrases from the box.

> best friend   have a lot in common
> a good sense of humour   enjoyed his company
> colleagues   get to know her   stranger
> lost touch   keep in touch   ex-girlfriend
> friend of a friend

1 It has been really nice seeing you again. Let's try and _____.

2 She always makes me laugh. She has _____.

3 Our relationship has finished so she's my _____ now.

4 I've met him once or twice at parties. He's a _____.

5 I'd like to _____ better because she seems very friendly.

6 I'm going out on Friday with a few _____ from work.

7 Mario and I have a good relationship because we like the same things. We _____.

8 He was a _____ who I met on a train, but we talked a lot and I _____.

9 I speak to Lucy every day on the phone. She's my _____.

10 Unfortunately we _____ when we left university.

2 Complete the adverts with prepositions.

> *Are you interested* (1) _____ *books?*
> Would you like to spend time with friends talking (2) _____ books you have read?
> *Join us at the BOOK CLUB every Friday.*

> ● Do you worry (3) _____ your weight?
> ● Are you keen (4) _____ exercise but not good (5) _____ team sports?
> Join **Solutions Fitness Centre** and we'll help you feel better.

Grammar | auxiliary verbs

3 a Put the words in the correct order to make questions.

1 are sports at good you ?

2 brothers any got or has sisters he ?

3 are how they old ?

4 you German do like studying ?

5 America been have you to ?

6 today you seen have boss your ?

7 you shops did go yesterday the to ?

b Write short answers to the questions in Ex. 3a. Use auxiliary verbs where possible.

4 a Make questions from the prompts.

1 What/sports/you/interested in?

2 You/been/skiing/recently?

3 She/like/listening to/music?

4 Mozart/play/the violin?

5 Your parents/enjoy/the concert/last night?

6 You/speak to Frances/yesterday?

7 Clara/had/her baby yet?

8 You/born/in Turin?

b Match the answers to the questions in Ex. 4a.

a Yes, she does. She's really keen on Mozart.

b No, I wasn't. I was born in Rome.

c Yes, I did. She called me last night.

d Yes, they did. They loved it.

e Yes, he did. He taught himself when he was five years old.

f I love skiing and watching football.

g Yes, she has. He's called Jack.

h Yes, I have. I went to Switzerland last week.

> Want to be fluent (6) _____ English, but you don't want to spend all your money (7) _____ a language course?
> Join the **English Language Club**.
> Students from all over the world belong (8) _____ the club so come and learn about new cultures too.
> **ELC**

4

Pronunciation

5　**a** **1.1** Say the following numbers. Listen and check.

1	19.5	4	6,156
2	47%	5	72.9%
3	3 h 15 mins	6	180

b **1.2** Cover the tapescript. Listen and write the numbers you hear.

1 ＿＿＿＿＿　　4 ＿＿＿＿＿

2 ＿＿＿＿＿　　5 ＿＿＿＿＿

3 ＿＿＿＿＿　　6 ＿＿＿＿＿

> **TAPESCRIPT**
>
> | 1 | 8.967 | 3 | 645 | 5 | 3,642 |
> |---|---|---|---|---|---|
> | 2 | 92% | 4 | 27% | 6 | €410 |

Reading

6　Read the article and choose the best title.

1　Young people – are they big spenders?

2　China – the richest country in the world?

3　Shenzen – a changing city: how people spend their money

7　Read the article again. Are these sentences true (T) or false (F)?

1　How you spend your money does not depend on how old you are. ☐

2　The city of Shenzen has become richer because professional people have moved there for work. ☐

3　People now spend twice as much money on education as before. ☐

4　Most families in Shenzen have a mobile phone. ☐

5　Seven out of ten families in Shenzen have a car. ☐

6　People spend more money on visiting other places. ☐

7　More people eat in restaurants than before. ☐

8　Underline four words or expressions in the article which can be used for making generalisations.

It's no surprise that what you spend your money on depends on your age, where you live, how big your family is, and how much money you earn. But have you ever thought about how people change
5　their spending when a whole city starts to get richer?

Shenzen, in China, has attracted lots of talented professionals in the last few years, and the average man or woman there now earns more
10　than in any other medium-sized city in China. So what do these Shenzen residents tend to spend their money on?

The first thing is education. This is very expensive in China, and professional people
15　generally spend more than 1000 yuan each on education. This is one and a half times more money than they spent in 1995. They also spend four times as much on communications and telephones. In every 100 households there are
20　now 93 mobile phones and 54 home computers. People have started to buy bigger houses. They now usually have an average five square metres more space in their apartments, and some have even bought second houses too.

25　The biggest change, however, has been in the number of people buying cars. In 1995 only four or five families in every 100 owned a car. Now this number has risen to seven in every 100, and it is continuing to rise.

30　Earning more money also means that the people of Shenzen can enjoy their leisure time more. Tourism is up by 18%. During the last Spring festival more than 200,000 Shenzen people travelled abroad. Perhaps this is where
35　they started to eat out in restaurants, because for many people in Shenzen, and particularly for younger people, not cooking at home is another new trend.

Vocabulary | computers

1 Complete the sentences with suitable words from the box.

> download research access website
> online delete down message

1 **A:** Have you heard from Martin recently?
  B: Yes, he sent me a _____ this morning.
2 I tend to do a lot of _____ on the Internet for my work.
3 I'm having problems with my computer. It won't shut _____.
4 It's going to take four minutes to _____ this file from the Internet.
5 I prefer to shop _____ because I can do it from the office.
6 I found a great _____ for information on politicians.
7 If you don't need that file anymore, can you please _____ it.
8 Is there anywhere near here where I can _____ the Internet?

Is there anywhere near here where I can access the Internet?

Grammar | Present Simple vs Present Continuous

2 Some of the <u>underlined</u> verbs are in the wrong tense. Put them into the correct tense.

1 Let's go out. It <u>doesn't rain</u> now.
2 I <u>go</u> to the gym on Tuesdays and Thursdays.
3 The earth <u>is going</u> around the sun.
4 Can you turn the kettle off? The water <u>boils</u>.
5 We should leave soon. It <u>gets</u> late.
6 I can't hear him very well. What is he <u>talking</u> about?
7 <u>Do</u> you <u>use</u> the computer now? I'd like to check my email.
8 We <u>stay</u> with some friends at the moment.
9 Can you see that woman? She <u>tries</u> to steal that car!
10 **A:** What job <u>are</u> you <u>doing</u>?
  B: I'm a journalist, but I<u>'m not working</u> at the moment.

3 Put the verbs in the correct form, Present Simple or Present Continuous.

1 **A:** How is your English?
  B: Not bad. It _____ (get) better.
2 I usually _____ (finish) work at six o'clock, and it _____ (take) me ten minutes to walk home.
3 You should turn your lights on. It _____ (get) dark.
4 _____ you always _____ (listen) to music in the car?
5 I _____ (live) with my parents until I can find an apartment to buy.
6 Hurry up, Anna! We _____ (wait) for you.
7 This train _____ (be) always late!
8 I _____ usually _____ (not enjoy) parties.
9 We _____ (go) out most evenings.
10 **A:** What's that noise?
  B: It's Jude. He _____ (play) the trumpet.

Writing

4 Put the lines in the correct order to complete the informal email.

Hi Diego,

Thanks for your message. I received your email this morning ...

- ☐ **a** It is very hard work
- ☐ **b** I hope so ...
- ☐ **c** I'm sorry I haven't been in touch for such a long time ...
- ☐ **d** My company is buying a factory in China,
- ☐ **e** ... so I have to travel a lot.
- ☐ **f** ... because it would be great to see you there.
- ☐ **g** ... and it was great to hear all your news.
- ☐ **h** ... but I am enjoying it.
- ☐ **i** Are you coming to Rico's wedding?
- ☐ **j** ... but I'm very busy in my new job.

I hope to see you soon anyway. Take care.

Matteo

Listening

5 **a** **[1.3]** Cover the tapescript. Listen to the psychologist. What is she talking about?

1 girlfriends and boyfriends
2 email relationships
3 penfriends
4 work relationships

TAPESCRIPT

Email friends can help you enjoy your day at work, but don't expect too much from them as many email friends prefer to stay online only.

One woman I spoke to recently, Patricia, met a new colleague, Howard, at a conference. They got on really well and on Monday morning when Patricia got to work there was an email from Howard in her inbox.

She replied and they started an email relationship. They found that they had a lot in common. They shared memories, and talked about their workmates. Sometimes they swapped more than twelve emails a day, only stopping if one of them had a meeting. Patricia looked forward to receiving Howard's emails when she arrived at work.

After a few weeks, however, Patricia asked Howard if he wanted to meet up after work, but he always found an excuse not to. Then she received a really strange email from him explaining how he didn't want to have a relationship and how he had decided to stop emailing her. That was the end of the story, and she never heard from him again.

You see, an email relationship takes a lot less energy and organising than a face-to-face relationship. So a lot of people who don't really want the responsibility of a relationship will try email friends instead. It's easier and, if you have an argument, you can always just shut down your computer!

b Listen again. Choose the correct answers.

1 Email friends are good for
   A going out with after work.
   B spending time while you are at work.

2 Patricia and Howard
   A were old friends.
   B met at a conference.

3 They talked about
   A their colleagues.
   B their problems.

4 They usually wrote
   A lots of emails every day.
   B one or two emails a day.

5 Patricia asked Howard to
   A meet her after work.
   B stop emailing her.

6 Howard
   A wanted to go to the cinema with Patricia.
   B didn't want to meet her in person.

7 Email relationships use
   A more energy than face-to-face relationships.
   B less energy than face-to-face relationships.

8 The advantage of an email relationship is that if you have an argument, you can
   A switch off your computer.
   B meet for a coffee.

Grammar | Present Perfect vs Past Simple

1 Complete the gaps in the text with verbs from the box.

> has learnt   have always wanted   has spent
> flew   hasn't got married   hasn't taught
> has done   have always admired
> has gone   met

I (1) _____ _____ _____ my sister. She is younger than me and (2) _____ _____ _____ or had children. She (3) _____ _____ her life travelling and living in different countries. She (4) _____ _____ lots of different jobs and she (5) _____ _____ to speak four or five different languages. Now, she (6) _____ _____ to Thailand. I (7) _____ _____ _____ to go there. She (8) _____ to Bangkok last month and (9) _____ a man who offered her a job in his school. She (10) _____ _____ children before so she is looking forward to it. It is another new experience.

2 Complete the second sentence so that it means the same as the first. Use the verbs in brackets. Put the verbs in the correct form.

1 He became a lawyer in 2002.
He _____ 2002. (be)

2 My parents started keeping dogs when I was six years old.
My parents _____ I was six years old. (keep)

3 She went to Paris last Tuesday.
She _____ Tuesday. (be)

4 I met them two years ago.
I _____ two years. (know)

5 She bought that car five years ago.
She _____ five years. (have)

6 Alice isn't here because she went to the bank.
Alice _____ to the bank. (go)

7 They got married 25 years ago.
They _____ 25 years. (be)

8 They started working together in 2004.
They _____ 2004. (work)

Vocabulary | for and since

3 Some sentences below have mistakes. Correct the mistakes and tick the correct sentences.

1 I haven't seen Maria for a couple of months.
2 I've had a headache since lunchtime.
3 I haven't had a cigarette since three weeks!
4 I've known Julia for we went to university.
5 I've lived here since ten years.
6 I have studied English since I was at school.
7 Have you been here since a long time?
8 I've had a bad cold for last weekend.
9 I haven't slept since the moment I heard the news.
10 I haven't eaten anything for nine o'clock this morning.

Pronunciation | /æ/ or /ə/ ?

4 **a** Put the words in bold in the table below according to the pronunciation of the underlined a. Is it /æ/ apple, or /ə/ comp<u>a</u>ny?

1 C<u>a</u>n I have a **cig<u>a</u>rette**?
2 I'd like some **<u>a</u>dvice**.
3 He's very good at **<u>a</u>thletics**.
4 What's **h<u>a</u>ppened**?
5 The **music<u>a</u>ns h<u>a</u>ve <u>a</u>rrived**.
6 The **c<u>a</u>t** looks **comfort<u>a</u>ble**.

/æ/ apple	/ə/ comp<u>a</u>ny

b **1.4** Listen and check your answers. Practise saying the sentences.

Reading

5 Read the text about the Schumacher brothers, then tick the correct summary.

A The brothers don't get on well because they are too competitive. ☐

B The brothers have a good relationship, even when they race against each other. ☐

C Their relationship has got worse since they started racing. ☐

BROTHERLY LOVE?

Michael and Ralf Schumacher are perhaps the most famous Formula One racing brothers in the world but, until recently, Ralf has always been overshadowed by his older brother. Now Ralf is winning too. So what has changed?

Many people think that the change started when their mother died. This was a very important moment for Ralf, who was particularly close to her. Others suggest that he has been affected by the criticism he has received over the years from his brother, and from the media.

Or perhaps it is simply that he is driving a faster car. 'I wouldn't attribute it all to Ralf,' Michael told the German newspaper Bild am Sonntag, 'he's finally got a car he can get something out of.'

The relationship between the two brothers may be changing on the track but it stays the same off it: very warm and friendly.

'We were fighting against each other in the last few years in Formula One and our relationship didn't change so I see no reason why it should change now,' said Ralf. 'I love my brother even if I'm battling him for the championship.'

The main difference seems to be that they discuss racing a lot less these days. 'We have been talking less about Formula One since I've been in the same league as my brother,' Ralf said. 'I'll give you an example. In Australia we went out for dinner and spent three hours together and I swear we didn't say a single word about Formula One. And that hasn't changed.'

6 Read the text again and answer the questions.

1 Has Ralf Schumacher always won Formula One races?
2 Did Ralf have a good relationship with his mother?
3 What three things might have changed the way Ralf drives?
4 What does Michael think has been the most important factor in Ralf's success?
5 Do the brothers have a good relationship when they are not working?
6 When they go out together now, do they talk a lot about racing?

Vocabulary

1 Use the words in the box to complete the text.

> access   get   website   about   belong
> best friends   lost   common   strangers
> keen   ex-girlfriend

The Friends Reunited (1) _____ helps (2) _____ who have (3) _____ touch to find each other again. More than 11,000,000 people (4) _____ to the site, with over 63,000 schools, colleges and universities. If you're not (5) _____ on meeting with your old school friends, why not find someone who used to live near you? Over 500,000 old neighbours have met through the site, which covers 2,000,000 streets. And you don't need to worry (6) _____ the expense – the website is free to (7)_____. You just need to register. Then you can search the site to find old colleagues, school friends, housemates or first loves. One man said he just had a look to see what his (8)_____ was doing, and discovered that, 'She was married with four children.' On the new dating website, you can (9) _____ to know (10) _____ , to see if you have anything in (11) _____.

Auxiliary verbs

2 Write questions from the prompts.

1 you/live/in Thailand? Yes, I do.
2 you/see/James Bond film/last night? No, we didn't.
3 When/Sal/go/on holiday? Next week.
4 What/sports/you/interested in? Tennis and basketball.
5 You/enjoy/study? Yes, I do.
6 You/forget/your books? Yes, I have.
7 Tim/like/working for IBM? Yes, he does.
8 You/happy/in/your new flat? Yes, I am.
9 George G/win/the election? Yes, he did.
10 You/pass/all your exams? Yes, I have!

3 Write short answers to the questions.

1 Are you interested in history? Yes, I _____.
2 Does he write his own songs? Yes, _____ _____.
3 Have you ever thought about leaving France? No, I _____.
4 Can you lend me a pen? Yes, I _____.
5 Is the weather nice? Yes, _____ _____.
6 Did they call to confirm the booking? Yes, _____ _____.
7 Is she enjoying her new course? Yes, _____ _____.
8 Do they want to come to the show? Yes, _____ _____.
9 Have you finished playing on the computer? Yes, _____ _____.
10 Does the chef come from Italy? No, _____ _____.

Present Simple, Present Continuous, Present Perfect

4 Circle the correct option.

1 I tend to *use/am using/have using* emails rather than letters.
2 We *flying/fly/have flown* from Heathrow airport at 9.30a.m.
3 What *are/have/do* you enjoy spending your money on?
4 Private schools *are/are being/have been* very expensive in China nowadays.
5 It *isn't seeming/hasn't seemed/doesn't seem* like a good idea to me.
6 Do you want to borrow this book? I *am just finishing/'ve just finished/just finish* it, and it was brilliant!
7 I'm afraid she's busy at the moment. She *talks/has talked/'s talking* to someone on the other line.
8 I'm *trying/have trying/am try* to get fit, so I cycle to work every day.
9 I've *always enjoyed/'m always enjoying/'ve always enjoy* painting.
10 She works in the sales department, but I *can't remember/'m not remembering/haven't remembered* her name.

for/since

5 Complete the sentences with *for* or *since*.

1 I haven't heard from him _____ ages.
2 We've been touring _____ last month.
3 They've been gone _____ yesterday.
4 Have you been waiting _____ long?
5 I've played the guitar _____ I was sixteen years old.
6 She's staying there _____ a few weeks.
7 We haven't seen Horace _____ he left home.
8 We lived in Spain _____ fifteen years.
9 He's been crying _____ this morning.
10 We've wanted to tell you _____ the weekend.

6 Correct the mistakes in the sentences.

1 I've know her for a long time. We went to school together.
2 'Have you spoken to the manager?' 'Yes, I have done it this morning.'
3 When have they got married?
4 We haven't been in touch since a long time.
5 When did you started working together?
6 I've never did watch that programme.
7 It's the funniest book I've never read.
8 She have had a hair cut.
9 I've just start to learn Tai Kwando.
10 I haven't did sign the contract yet.

7 Complete the dialogues using the verbs in brackets.

A: (1) _____ you ever _____ to San Francisco? (be)
B: Yes, I (2) _____ there a few years ago. (go)
A: (3) _____ you _____ it? (enjoy)
B: I (4) _____ it was fantastic! (think)
A: (5) _____ you _____ squash regularly? (play)
B: Yes. I (6) _____ quite good at it. (be)
A: How long (7)_____ you _____ for? (play)
B: I (8) _____ about six years ago. (start)
A: (9) _____ you _____ to play on Sunday? (want)
B: That (10) _____ like a great idea! (sound)

Phrasal verbs

8 Complete the sentences with words from the box.

> told on up brought into
> looked take up joined got

1 I grew _____ in New Orleans.
2 I was _____ up to enjoy music.
3 I think I _____ after my father, because he was very musical too.
4 My mother always _____ me off for not practising the piano enough.
5 I _____ on well with Joey, the singer, who lived next door.
6 He was a professional musician, so I _____ up to him for that.
7 When I left home, I carried _____ playing.
8 I gave _____ playing when I started my new job.
9 I got _____ playing music again last year.
10 Now I've _____ up with some friends and we play in a band together at weekends.

Prepositional/phrasal verbs

9 Choose the correct option.

1 He *told/took/said* me off for being late.
2 The factory was taken *in/up/over* by a German business.
3 I have always looked *over/down/up* to my older brother.
4 My mother looks *up to/after/on* Charlie when I am at work.
5 He has used *over/up/by* all the paper.
6 We were brought *on/in/up* to eat everything on our plates.
7 I *grew/belong/take* up in the countryside, but moved to the city for work.
8 I generally get *off/on/to* well with people at work.
9 I don't see him very often but we keep *in/off/on* touch by email.
10 I'm very organised. I take *on/off/after* my mother.

2.1 Media

Vocabulary | newspapers

1 Choose the best word.

1 Let's put this story on the *headline/front page/section*.

2 Did you read that *interview/report/celebrity* with Michael Jackson?

3 Today's *main story/free press/review* was about a French politician.

4 You can read about new books in the *headline/journalist/review section*.

5 A lot of *front pages/journalists/reports* have interviewed her, but no one really knows her.

6 *The free press/The daily papers/Online news* on the Internet is more up-to-date than newspapers.

2 Find the words in the puzzle to match the definitions below.

c	e	s	e	c	t	i	o	n	s
e	d	d	e	h	a	v	c	y	u
l	i	n	t	e	r	v	i	e	w
e	t	d	j	a	b	u	f	s	a
b	o	s	u	d	a	i	l	y	a
r	r	f	c	l	v	k	o	d	d
i	a	r	t	i	c	l	e	c	v
t	f	r	o	n	t	p	a	g	e
y	x	a	w	e	q	o	p	j	r
j	o	u	r	n	a	l	i	s	t

1 Someone who writes news stories. _____

2 Where the most important stories go in the newspaper. The _____

3 The title of a news story. _____

4 A type of news story. _____

5 A famous person. _____

6 Publicity for a product or business (abbreviation). _____

7 A question-and-answer discussion. _____

8 Separate parts of a newspaper, eg Sports, Finance. _____

9 A newspaper that is printed every day. A _____ paper.

10 The person responsible for the content of a newspaper. _____

Grammar | passive

3 Complete the second sentence with no more than three words so that it means the same as the first.

Mr Ford founded the company in 1926.
The company <u>was founded</u> in 1926.

1 The editor doesn't write many articles.
Not many articles _____ the editor.

2 Japanese workers made the product.
The product _____ Japanese workers.

3 A group of large banks organised the meeting.
The meeting _____ a group of large banks.

4 The engineer has fixed the photocopier.
The photocopier has _____.

5 The player signed the contract today.
The contract _____ today.

6 He switches off the machines at night.
The machines _____ at night.

7 You can find branches of our company in most countries in the world.
Branches of our company can _____ in most countries.

8 I have contacted the client.
The client _____.

4 Complete the form using the passive in the correct tense.

NewsUp Magazine

will (1)_____ (deliver) to your home every Saturday.

All questions must (2)_____ (answer).

How did you hear about **NewsUp**?
Tick a box:
- I (3)_____ (tell) about **NewsUp** by a friend. ☐
- I saw **NewsUp** in a shop. ☐

Tick a box for your choice of **free gift**:
- DVD of news highlights of the year. ☐
- Hardback copy of The Newsmakers. ☐

Your **free gift** will (4)_____ (sent) to your home address.

NewsUp (5)_____ (print) on recycled paper.

How to ... | give opinions, agree and disagree

5 Complete the dialogue with words from the box.

> neither   reckon   definitely   opinion
> depends   sure   so   what   in

A: (1)_____ do you think of Reality TV?

B: (2)_____ my opinion, it's a complete waste of time. What's your (3)_____?

A: I'm not (4)_____. I (5)_____ it can be quite entertaining.

B: I don't think (6)_____.

A: It (7)_____ on the programme. Some of them are good, but I'd never watch them all day.

B: Me (8)_____. Only TV addicts watch Reality TV all day.

A: (9)_____!

Reading

6 a Read about a newspaper with a difference and answer the questions below.

1 Who normally chooses the news we read: *readers/editors*?

2 What news do you think is most popular: *stories about international business/gossip about famous people*?

3 How many people do you think read news on the Internet regularly: *about 50%/fewer than 30%*?

b Choose the best headline for the story.

1 Chilean newspaper celebrates its birthday ☐

2 Chile paper lets readers choose the news ☐

3 Chile's journalists stop writing serious news ☐

c Are these sentences true (T) or false (F)?

1 LUN was always a very successful newspaper. ☐

2 LUN uses internet technology to find out which stories are popular. ☐

3 LUN's most popular articles are usually very serious stories. ☐

4 Augustine Edwards thinks LUN is popular because it has stories that people want to read. ☐

5 At the moment LUN pays more money to the journalists if they write popular stories. ☐

6 At least 70% of Chileans *don't* click on their favourite stories on www.lun.com. ☐

A newspaper with a difference

It was 102 years old, boring and unpopular. But now *Las Ultimas Noticias* (LUN: The Latest News), has become one of Chile's favourite newspapers. Employees at LUN say it's a revolution in journalism. Critics say it's rubbish.

In 2001 LUN started counting the number of clicks on each story on its website (www.lun.com). The clicks tell the editors which stories are popular and which are not. If an article gets a lot of clicks, the newspaper continues the story the following day, or finds similar ones. If an article gets only a few clicks, the story is killed. According to Augustine Edwards, the newspaper's publisher, LUN reflects the changing values and interests of Chile.

So, what news did readers choose when world leaders arrived in Santiago for an important trade meeting? One of the top stories was about where US politician Colin Powell went to dinner and what he ate (prawns with couscous). Another popular story was about which politicians gave the best tips to the waiters (the Japanese).

The critics say LUN now has no serious news. Edwards replies, 'I'm focused not on what people should read, but what they want to read. I want my journalists to write for the people, not for me or their editors.' He even plans to pay his journalists according to the number of clicks their stories get.

One question remains. Only 30% of the country has Internet access: the richest 30%. So is LUN really a reflection of 'the changing values and interests of Chile'?

Vocabulary | TV programmes

1 Complete the sentences with words from the box.

> soap newsreaders contestants audience
> documentary chat shows microphone
> quiz show

1 The _____ wasn't working so no one could hear him!

2 *University Challenge* is a type of _____ for students, with questions about many subjects.

3 The _____ on *Mastermind* have two minutes to answer as many questions as they can, on one subject.

4 Famous actors usually go on _____ to publicise their new movies.

5 I watched a very interesting _____ about wild animals in Africa.

6 My favourite ——— is about a rich family from Dallas. I watch it twice a week.

7 *Big Brother* has a huge _____. I don't know why. I think it's really boring.

8 In my country, _____ are usually middle-aged men. The public trusts them to tell the truth!

How to ... | deal with problems

2 Put the words in the correct order to complete the dialogues.

1 **A:** problem what's the ? _____
   B: computer it's my. working isn't properly it. _____
   A: switching off try it. _____
   B: that tried I've. _____

2 **A:** the matter what's ? _____
   B: car son's it's toy my. keeps stopping it. _____
   A: out the run have batteries ? _____
   B: right yes, you're oh! _____

3 **A:** the what's lift with wrong ? _____
   B: order out it's of. _____
   A: I call shall engineers the ? _____
   B: called I've them just. _____

Grammar | *who, whose, which, where*

3 Choose the correct phrases from the box to complete the sentences. Use *who/whose/which/where* to join the two phrases. You will need to omit some words.

> his wife won the lottery   it makes jewellery
> her films always make money
> we stayed there last year
> you can surf there all year
> it looks best on you   they designed my house
> they are always honest

1 That's the man _____.
2 I like people _____.
3 That's the hotel _____.
4 Ella works in a factory _____.
5 Laguna has a big beach _____.
6 I spoke to the architects _____.
7 Black is the colour _____.
8 Donna is the type of director _____.

4 Complete the sentences using *who/which/where/whose*. Are they true (T) or false (F)?

1 An audience is a group of people _____ act in a show. ☐

2 A microphone is a technological tool _____ makes your voice quiet. ☐

3 Tecwen Whittock is the man _____ cough can be heard on *Who Wants to be a Millionaire?* ☐

4 A studio is a place _____ many live TV programmes are made. ☐

5 A contestant is someone _____ asks the questions on a quiz show. ☐

6 *Fix* is a verb _____ means *find a solution to a problem*. ☐

7 A newsreader is a person _____ job is to read the news. ☐

8 *Who Wants to be a Millionaire?* is a quiz show _____ has become world famous. ☐

Reading

5 **a** Read the text and choose the best endings for the sentences below.

1 Janet Cooke was
   A a very poor woman.
   B a journalist.
   C a newspaper editor.

2 She invented a story about
   A a child living a difficult life.
   B a man called Jimmy.
   C the government.

3 The city government
   A fired Cooke.
   B tried to find the boy.
   C didn't believe the story.

4 Stephen Glass created
   A a magazine.
   B a false identity for himself.
   C fake papers to pretend he was telling
      the truth.

5 Stephen Glass was caught
   A quickly.
   B by the police.
   C after many years.

6 Jayson Blair pretended to
   A interview many people.
   B work for the *New York Times*.
   C be a journalist.

b Find the words or expressions in bold that mean:

1 people who break into technological systems illegally _____

2 was revealed _____

3 top journalist _____

4 removed from a job _____

5 demanded _____

6 in a stressful situation _____

When no news is real news – the journalists who lied and got caught

Open a newspaper and you expect to read, more or less, the truth. So what happens when it turns out that journalists invent their stories? Ask Stephen Glass or Jayson Blair or Janet Cooke. They all spent parts of their careers inventing stories before being caught and **fired**.

Imagine the scene: Washington DC, 1980. Janet Cooke writes a long article for *The Washington Post* describing the world of eight-year-old Jimmy, a child living in terrible conditions in the poorest part of the city. She writes about every detail of his life, even describing the 'baby-smooth skin of his thin brown arms'. The story shocks Washington, and Cooke wins a Pulitzer Prize for outstanding journalism. But when the city government tries to find Jimmy to help him, Cooke goes quiet. **Under pressure**, she eventually admits that Jimmy doesn't exist.

Stephen Glass, a **star reporter** at *The New Republic* magazine, invented stories for years. 'My life was one very long process of lying and lying again to work out how to cover those other lies,' he says. Glass made great efforts to avoid getting caught. He created fake notes, fake faxes, fake email addresses; he even designed a website for a company that didn't exist. Eventually, he got caught when he wrote a story about a 15-year-old boy at a conference of computer **hackers**. His editor **insisted** on seeing the conference room. Of course, there was no conference room. And no conference either. And no 15-year-old boy. Glass's career as a journalist was finished, but he wrote a novel about his life, *The Fabulist*.

The most recent case was Jayson Blair. A 27-year-old journalist for the New York Times, Blair invented details for at least 36 of the 73 articles he wrote in his final seven months with the newspaper. He frequently pretended that he was doing interviews with people all over the US, from Ohio to Texas, when in fact he was simply inventing the stories in New York, or copying them from other media. When the truth **came out** in 2002, the media world was shocked.

The message for us, the public? Don't believe everything you read, even if it comes from your favourite, trusted newspaper!

Vocabulary | regular and irregular verbs

1 Underline the correct form of the verbs.

1 I *wake up/awoke up/woke up* early this morning.

2 He *drawed/drew/draws* a lot of pictures when he was young.

3 When his father died, Peter Morton *inherit/ inheritted/inherited* one million pounds.

4 We *flew/flied/flown* to France.

5 She *catched/cought/caught* the 5.50 train.

6 We *faught/fought/fighted* hard for ninety minutes, but still didn't win the game.

7 I *forgotten/forgetted/forgot* to pack my sunglasses.

8 Last year, problems with production *costed/ cast/cost* the company $50,000.

9 At 7.00 yesterday morning two prisoners *escapped/escaped/escope*.

10 I *cuted/cut/cutted* my hand this morning.

Pronunciation

2 Which verb ending sounds different? Choose the odd one out.

1 A jumped B looked C hated D stopped

2 A waved B lived C seemed D helped

3 A shouted B watched C printed D wanted

4 A loved B filled C complained D booked

5 A believed B located C decided
   D reminded

6 A shocked B missed C posted D kissed

3 There are three or four syllables in each line. Count and write the numbers in the boxes.

1 A: I asked you. ☐
   B: I responded! ☐

2 A: They attacked! ☐
   B: We defended! ☐

3 A: We waited there. ☐
   B: He returned. ☐

4 A: She touched him. ☐
   B: They both laughed. ☐

5 A: The child screamed. ☐
   B: She kissed him. ☐

Grammar | Past Simple and Past Continuous

4 Underline the best verb tense.

1 A: Where were you at 9a.m. this morning?
   B: I *drove/was driving* from Houston to San Diego.

2 She failed the test because she *didn't understand/wasn't understanding* the instructions.

3 He injured his knee while he *played/was playing* football.

4 I came to say goodnight yesterday but you *rested/were resting*.

5 We ate, paid the bill and *went/were going* home.

6 How *did you know/were you knowing* my name?

7 I saw you on the roof this morning! What *did you do/were you doing*?

8 We *talked/were talking* before you interrupted us!

5 Put the verbs in brackets into the Past Simple or Past Continuous.

Young boy, 5, discovered 300 kilometres from home

Police who (1)_____ (look) for a lost five-year-old boy eventually (2)_____ (find) him the next day. After getting separated from his family in a market, the boy, from Pekanbaru in Malaysia, (3)_____ (go) to a station, got onto a train, and was discovered in Padang, 300 kilometres away. 'He (4)_____ (be) very calm,' said the boy's mother. 'It was us, his family, who (5)_____ (worry) all night.'

Traffic jams make Angelenos feel at home

A recent study said that Los Angeles has the worst traffic in the United States. Last year Angelenos (6)_____ (spend) an average of 136 hours a year stuck in traffic. Only last week a man was arrested while he (7)_____ (brush) his teeth in the car, and drivers are regularly seen applying make-up and shaving. Police (8)_____ (say) that yesterday they (9)_____ (stop) a man who (10)_____ (drive) while playing on his laptop computer.

6 Look at the pictures and put the verbs in brackets into the Past Simple or Past Continuous.

1 Someone _____ (steal) my wallet while I _____ (not look).

2 I _____ (not know) you _____ (be) in town.

3 We _____ (not hear) the burglar because we _____ (listen) to loud music.

4 I _____ (drive) home when I _____ (see) a black cat at the side of the road.

5 Eve _____ (not take) the bus because it _____ (be) a beautiful day.

6 Josie _____ (meet) Clyde while they _____ (ski).

Listening

7 a **2.1** Cover the tapescript. Listen to the local news headlines and complete the notes.

1 Children eat too much _____, says nutritionist.

2 1,000 _____ to be destroyed.

3 _____ saves car crash victims.

4 Artist sells painting to _____.

TAPESCRIPT

And now for today's news headlines. A nutritionist says our children are eating too much fat. In Fincher, one thousand homes will be destroyed to build a shopping area. A taxi driver last night saved two lives after a car crash. And local artist Angela Witco sells a painting to rock star, Lee Santana.

---

b **2.2** Now listen to the news stories and answer the questions.

1 Who did Niall Smith study?

2 What food and drink should the children eat and drink less of?

3 What two things will the town of Fincher build in place of the houses?

4 When will the new houses be built?

5 Who did John Manley save?

6 Where exactly did he take them?

7 Where did Lee Santana see the painting?

8 How does Witco feel about selling her painting to Lee Santana?

TAPESCRIPT

Nutritionist Niall Smith from the Cambridge Think Tank on Diet and Health, says that our children eat too much fatty food. In a two-year study of 900 schoolchildren aged 11 to 15, Smith and his team found that children eat double the amount of fat recommended by nutritionists. Hamburgers, chips, chocolate and fizzy soft drinks were the biggest problems.

In the town of Fincher, one thousand homes will be knocked down to build a shopping area and car park. Local councillors say that the shopping area will revitalise Fincher town centre. They say new housing will be built next year.

A taxi driver, John Manley, has saved the lives of a husband and wife whose car crashed into a tree on Friday night. Manley pulled the couple from the car and drove them immediately to a London hospital in his taxi. They are now in a stable condition.

Painter Angela Witco has found a famous buyer for her work. Rock star and art lover Lee Santana bought Witco's painting *Trees in Winter* for an undisclosed sum. He saw the painting in a small art gallery in Manchester and fell in love with it immediately. Witco says she is extremely happy that her painting has found a good home.

Review and consolidation unit 2

Passives, Past Simple and Past Continuous

1 Put the verbs in brackets into the correct form.

1 Last year, over $4,000,000,000 _____ (spend) on computers.

2 I hurt my back while I _____ (work) in the garden.

3 When _____ (you realise) you had this great talent for tennis?

4 The car _____ (stop) by the police at 6.10a.m. They searched it immediately.

5 I _____ (not go) to the party because I had too much work to do.

6 Penicillin _____ (discover) by accident.

7 Who _____ (talk) to when I saw you this morning? I've never seen her before.

8 They didn't hear the news because they _____ (stay) on a desert island at that time.

9 I _____ (not know) you had the same birthday as me!

10 This type of food can _____ (eat) as a starter or as a main course.

Passives and Past Simple vs Continuous

2 **a** Match the first halves of the sentences, 1–8, to the second halves, a–h.

1 Robin Kruger wasn't caught while he was [d][1]

2 In his left hand he was carrying a small gun and [ ][ ]

3 A few hours later, he was captured at his home, [ ][ ]

4 He gave a note to Melanie Joseph, who [ ][ ]

5 Kruger was wearing sunglasses and a hat [ ][ ]

6 The note said 'I have a gun in my hand. [ ][ ]

7 Miss Joseph took the note and gave [ ][ ]

8 Policeman Don Callow explained, 'Kruger's note was [ ][8]

a was working there as a cashier.

b where he was counting his money.

c Give me £10,000 in cash.'

d trying to rob a bank, but very soon afterwards.

e written on the back of an envelope with his address on it.'

f in his right he had a bag for the money.

g him the money, and he walked out.

h when he walked into the bank.

b Now put the sentences in the correct order to make the story. The first and the last sentences have been done.

c <u>Underline</u> five examples of the Past Continuous, and circle three examples of the passive.

Defining relative clauses

3 Join the sentence pairs to make single sentences. Use *who/which/where/whose*. Change *a/an* to *the* where necessary, and delete any unnecessary words.

The Vatican City is a state. The Pope lives there.
The Vatican City is the state where the Pope lives.

1 Graceland is a place. Elvis Presley died there.

2 Franz Kafka was a writer. He wrote a story about a man who became an insect.

3 St Petersburg is a city. It used to be called Leningrad.

4 Rodin was a sculptor. He made *The Thinker*.

5 *Titanic* is a famous film. It cost $200,000,000 to make.

6 Malibu is a beach in California. Hundreds of celebrities live there.

7 Vivaldi was a composer. His most famous work was *The Four Seasons*.

8 Istanbul is a city. It is built on two continents – Europe and Asia.

4 Complete the sentences using the prompts and the passive so that they mean the same as the first sentences. Use three or four words including the words in brackets.

1 That's the boy! Someone gave him my bicycle.
That's the boy _____ my bicycle! (was)

2 These are great stories. People tell them from generation to generation.
These are the great stories _____ from generation to generation. (told)

3 He's an artist. People buy his paintings for thousands of Euros.
He's the artist _____ for thousands of Euros. (sold)

4 That's the old country house. I was born there.
That's the old country house _____. (was)

5 It's a type of pen. You can use it under water.
It's a type of pen _____ under water. (be)

6 These are the tourists. Someone has stolen their bags.
These are the tourists _____ stolen. (been)

7 He's the master criminal. We must stop him!
He's the master criminal _____. (stopped)

Irregular verbs

5 What is the past tense of each of these verbs? Underline the odd one out in each group.

1 A sell B teach C buy D fight
2 A move B own C clean D blow
3 A decide B shout C want D swim
4 A know B play C fly D grow
5 A cost B cut C run D hit
6 A come B speak C choose D wake
7 A wash B draw C mix D kiss
8 A get B go C forget D shoot
9 A deliver B put C move D show
10 A bring B catch C stop D think

How to …

6 **a** Complete these sentences by adding one word.

1 My opinion, we should buy the black sofa, not the blue one. _____ ☐
2 What you think of that new Bruce Willis film? _____ ☐
3 You think we should leave at 8.00, but I'm not sure that. _____ ☐
4 She said we could get in to the club free, but I don't think. _____ ☐
5 I'd love to go to the beach, but it depends the weather. _____ ☐
6 What's matter with your TV? The picture isn't very good, is it? _____ ☐
7 If your computer isn't working, try turning off and on again. _____ ☐
8 The photocopier is out order again. _____ ☐
9 The problem with your printer is that it's run out paper! _____ ☐
10 If the microwave breaks down again, call us and we can fix immediately. _____ ☐

b Match the sentences, 1–10, to the responses, a–j.

a Me too. I think it'll be sunny.
b It depends on the traffic, but I think 8.15 will be OK.
c Oh dear. We need some copies for this morning. Shall I call the engineers?
d Great. I'll keep your phone number then.
e It depends how expensive the black one is.
f It isn't working properly. I can only get two channels.
g OK, I'll try that.
h OK, I'll put some more in!
i I think it's brilliant. I love the action scenes.
j Me neither. We usually have to pay.

Vocabulary

7 **a** Put the words and phrases in the box into the correct columns.

> cameraman documentary journalist
> headline quiz show the front page
> soap newsreader celebrity
> review section editor article
> chat show main story contestant
> presenter advertisement

People	Types of TV programme	Things in a newspaper

b Use the words and phrases above to complete the sentences.

1 You can read about new books and films in the _____ of the Sunday paper.
2 We saw a _____ about wild animals in Africa on TV. It followed the movements of lions.
3 I watch this _____ every week. I love the characters.
4 I'd like to be a _____ because every day you can write interesting news stories.
5 One _____ on this quiz show got every answer right. He won $10,000!
6 I would hate to be a _____ like David Beckham or Julia Roberts. I prefer a quiet life.
7 I saw an interesting _____ in the newspaper for a job in Hawaii.
8 Did you read about the President? The story was on _____ of every newspaper!
9 That quiz show _____ is so bad he can't even say the questions properly!
10 I read an _____ in the newspaper about new technology. It was very long, but it was interesting and well-written.

Vocabulary | home

1 Complete the sentences with the words and phrases in the box.

> good view ceilings condition
> drive wooden cramped cellar
> lift fireplace attic

1 It was cold, so we lit a fire and sat around the _____.

2 I prefer _____ floors without carpets.

3 You can see the sea from the window. The flat has a very _____.

4 The apartment is very modern and in good _____.

5 There's no _____ so you have to use the stairs.

6 I love these old houses because they have such high _____.

7 I've put all the old furniture up in the _____.

8 We keep the wine in the _____ because it is very cool down there.

9 We like the flat but it is a bit small and _____.

10 You can park the car outside the house, in the _____.

Grammar | Present Continuous vs *going to*/*will* for future

2 Complete the sentences using the words in brackets and *will* or *going to*.

1 A: Why are you moving all those books?
   B: _____ offices tomorrow. (I/change)

2 A: What would you like to drink?
   B: _____ some mineral water, please. (I/have)

3 A: I don't know how to work this computer programme.
   B: Don't worry. _____ you. (I/show)

4 A: Have you decided where to go on your birthday?
   B: Yes, it's all planned. _____ to that new restaurant I told you about. (We/go)

5 A: Did you remember to call David?
   B: No, I forgot. _____ it now. (I/do)

6 A: _____ to the shops. Do you want a sandwich? (I/go)
   B: No thanks. _____ something later. (I/get)

3 Add one or two words to complete each sentence.

1 I need some fresh air. I think I go for a walk.

2 you seeing Jack at the weekend?

3 What time Susannah coming?

4 We going to Berlin at the end of the month.

5 They've changed their minds. They're going to Thailand any more, they are to Greece.

6 Are you coming to the concert too? Great – we see you there then.

7 He doesn't like the new job so I don't think he stay there for very long.

8 'What are your plans for supper?' 'I cooking pizza.'

Writing | a formal letter

4 Replace the underlined phrases in the letter with phrases from the box to make it more formal.

> I was also very disappointed … I am writing to complain about … I expect to receive a full refund   Dear …   Yours sincerely
> I would also like …   In fact, …   In addition to this …   I look forward to receiving a satisfactory reply.   According to your website …

(1) Hello Mr Smith,

(2) This is a short letter to tell you that I think the accommodation that your company provides is not very good.

(3) Your website says that the apartments are all modern and in good condition. (4) But, the apartment I stayed in was built in the 1970s, and needed work doing to it. The floors in the kitchen and bathroom were broken and dirty. (5) And the washing machine was not working.

(6) I was also not happy to find that the apartment was a long way from the beach, and not 'within ten minutes' walk' as specified in the brochure.

I had to move to another apartment, which took me time and cost me money. I paid over 300 Euros as a deposit on your flat and now (7) I hope you will send me all the money back.

(8) And I want you to change the information on your website and in your brochures.

(9) I hope you will write to me soon.

(10) Best wishes,

Miguel Rodrigues

Reading

5 **a** Read the text and complete the table.

	Jean-Marc, Felicity and Yannick	Pat, John and Sally
Where is their house?		
How many bedrooms are there?		
Other features of the house/area.		
How much money does the hotel/bed and breakfast make?		
How do they spend their time?		
What do they want to get from the house swap?		

b What is different about this house swap?

HOUSE SWAP WITH A DIFFERENCE

Swapping your house with another family is one thing. But would you be happy to swap not just your house, but also your business? This is exactly what the following two families decided to do.

Jean-Marc, Felicity and Yannick (16) live in a huge villa in the south of France. The house has six guest bedrooms, a swimming pool, vineyards and extensive gardens. They run a hotel from the house, earning more than €50,000 per year. They employ two full-time staff so that they can take time off work to swim, eat good food, play golf and generally enjoy the Mediterranean lifestyle.

They decided to swap lives with John, Pat and Sally for one month. They hoped that the swap would be useful work experience for their daughter Yannick.

John, Pat and their daughter Sally live in Bongor, a seaside town in the north of England, famous for its fish and chips. They run a bed and breakfast, which has ten rooms, and earns €20,000 in the high season, and about €10,000 during the rest of the year. They work hard. John manages the finances and serves food and drinks to the guests. Sally works as a waitress and helps Pat in the kitchen. Pat does the shopping, cooking, cleaning the bedrooms, and anything else that needs to be done. Pat is exhausted and wants to spend a month in France, to see how different life could be.

We spoke to the couples after their swap to ask them how it went.

Listening

6 **a** **3.1** Cover the tapescript. Listen to Pat and Jean-Marc describing the house swap.

1 Was the swap a success for Pat?
2 Was the swap a success for Jean-Marc?

b Listen again and answer the questions about Pat.

1 Why was the house swap like a honeymoon?
2 What job did she have to do in the mornings?
3 What did they do with their free time?

c Now answer the questions about Jean-Marc.

4 Where did the English family live when they were at home?
5 Why didn't Jean-Marc like the traditional English breakfast?
6 Was the trip a success for Yannick?
7 Would they like to repeat the experience?

TAPESCRIPT

Pat: It was wonderful. It was probably the best thing I've ever done. When we arrived at this beautiful villa it was like being on honeymoon. There was hardly any work to do. There was a cleaner for the rooms, and the only cooking I had to do was to make coffee in the morning! We had lots of free time, so we travelled around the area and went sailing. It didn't feel like work at all – it was a wonderful holiday.

Jean-Marc: Well, we were very surprised to see how the English family lived. They had two very small rooms in the basement, underground, and all the nice bedrooms were used for the guests. Also I think they work too hard, because nobody helps them. They are always cooking and cleaning. I had to cook a traditional English breakfast, but it was terrible. I can't eat food like that because I think it is very bad for you. In France we have fresh bread, with jam and coffee. It is healthier, and easier to prepare too! It was an interesting experience, but I was very happy to come home, and I don't think Yannick learnt anything very useful. We wouldn't do it again.

Vocabulary | adjectives for describing place

1 **a** Match the adjectives in Box A to their opposites in Box B.

A	B
modern ugly tiny clean noisy dull	polluted enormous picturesque lively historic peaceful

b Use the words from Boxes A and B above to complete the sentences. Choose words with meanings similar to the words/phrases in brackets.

1 There is nobody on the beach at this time of year. It's very _____. (quiet)

2 We enjoyed walking around the _____ city centre. (old)

3 You must see Sofia's new room. It's _____. (very big)

4 The problem with big cities like Bangkok is that they are very _____. (dirty with fumes)

5 We had a fantastic time in Prague. It is such a _____ city. (there are lots of people doing lots of exciting things)

6 The view over the river from our hotel was very _____. (lovely to look at)

7 Brasilia is a _____ city, with a lot of office blocks. (new)

8 It was a small town and there was nothing to do there. It was a bit _____. (uninteresting)

Grammar | comparatives/superlatives

2 Complete the sentences with a comparative form of the words in the box.

> modern expensive long peaceful
> small heavy near bad

1 It's very noisy in here. Shall we go somewhere _____?

2 The meal was cheap. I expected it to be _____.

3 Your suitcase feels light. Mine is much _____.

4 The style is a bit old-fashioned. I was looking for something _____.

5 That hotel is a long way from the centre. Can't you find anything _____?

6 This table is enormous. Have you got anything _____?

7 The service in the restaurant was excellent. I thought it would be _____.

8 Have you got to leave tomorrow? Can't you stay a little bit _____?

3 Complete the sentences with a comparative or superlative form of the words in brackets.

1 London is not _____ city to live in. (good)

2 Hotels in Milan are _____ in Rome. (expensive)

3 Rio de Janeiro is _____ city I have ever been to. (hot)

4 Madrid is a busy city. The atmosphere in Barcelona is _____ . (relaxed)

5 Ravenna has some of the _____ mosaics in the world. (beautiful)

6 Istanbul is one of _____ cities I know. (lively)

7 Vienna is beautiful, but Prague was _____. (romantic)

8 People in Paris seem _____ than people in St Tropez. (busy)

Reading

4 Read the information about a new book. Tick the statements which are correct.

The book:

1 provides information about different cities in the USA. ☐

2 is a fictional description of life in New York. ☐

3 tells you which are the best and the worst cities to live in. ☐

4 describes twelve of the best European cities. ☐

5 might be useful for someone who is planning to move to the USA. ☐

Think your city is best?
See the latest rankings.

The latest issue of *Cities Ranked and Rated* is just out. This book describes the top cities in the USA. But what is it that makes a metropolis great (or bad)?

Are you thinking about relocating, or just curious how your city compares with others across the nation? Well, the answers to your questions are here, as featured in the annually updated book *Cities Ranked and Rated*. The book's authors, Bert Sterling and Peter Sander, talked to us about their findings.

5 Read the interview and match the questions 1–7 to the answers a–f.

1 And how about older people, who are starting to think about retirement? What do they look for? ☐

2 If I'm young and single, just starting out, what places would I find attractive? ☐

3 And what if I have a family with kids? Is that different? ☐

4 In general, what places make it to the top of the list? ☐

5 How did you decide who makes it to the top? ☐

6 Were there any surprises in your findings? ☐

7 And what about the bad news? Why does a city end up at the bottom of your list? ☐

a We look at over a hundred pieces of information about each place. We group those into nine categories including: economy and jobs, cost of living, climate, education, arts and culture. Then we press a button on the computer, and that's how we get the top ten.

b Cities with a university do especially well. They have plenty to do, nice city centres, pleasant surroundings and usually they aren't too crowded. The strength in higher education tends to affect all levels of education and most have excellent health care facilities. Then there are the state capitals, which tend to be clean, have a good economic situation and lots of cultural facilities – these are also good.

c Yes, quite a few. For instance, highly ranked cities are found all across the country, not just on the sunny coastlines like everybody thinks. There are a few interesting cities that we call the 'Big City Bargains'. These are big cities with a low cost of living, like Pittsburgh and Indianapolis.

d Areas at the bottom typically have high levels of unemployment and crime and a high cost of living combined with low levels of education, few facilities and not much to do. However, most of these cities recognise that there are problems and they are actively working to improve.

e Younger single people are interested in places with jobs where they can build their careers and make money. They want lively cities with lots to do, and of course lots of other single people too! Of course, the top ten cities would all be good places to live, but for singles in particular we would choose the Norfolk area in Virginia and San Antonio, Texas.

f Yes. Families look for many things, including good and affordable housing, quality education and more daytime facilities like parks, museums and outdoor recreation.

g Well, that is the important thing about this book, it won't just help you decide where you should be now, it'll help you to plan for the future, too. People who are planning to retire soon are thinking more about health care, leisure and the overall cost of living and less about jobs, housing costs and education.

6 Choose the best answers.

1 The authors decided on the top cities by
   A asking people about their favourite cities.
   B looking at the population of each city.
   C comparing statistics about each city.

2 According to the book, university cities
   A have a lot of crime.
   B are nice cities to live in.
   C usually have too many people.

3 Cities with lots of people in higher education also tend to
   A have a low cost of living.
   B have good hospitals and doctors.
   C come near the bottom of the list.

4 The top cities
   A are found on the coasts.
   B are cheap to live in.
   C are spread across the country.

5 'Big City Bargains' are cities which
   A are cheap to live in.
   B are expensive to live in.
   C have a low standard of living.

6 Cities at the bottom of the list
   A don't realise that there is a problem.
   B have a lot of people who do not work.
   C are cheap to live in.

7 Young single people look for cities
   A where they can get good jobs.
   B where there are a lot of parks and museums.
   C which are cheap to live in.

8 Older people are not so interested in
   A parks and museums.
   B the price of houses.
   C the cost of living.

Vocabulary | compound nouns

1 Complete the sentences with compound nouns from the box.

> answering machine   washing machine
> central heating   air conditioning
> video player   alarm clock   burglar alarm
> mobile phone

1 Could I borrow your _____? I need to wake up early tomorrow.

2 Can you put all the dirty clothes in the _____?

3 It's hot! Shall we turn on the _____?

4 My flat is very cold because the _____ isn't working.

5 You can call her on her _____. The number is 0776 237658.

6 They stole everything. We've got a _____ but I forgot to switch it on.

7 Shan wasn't at home but I left a message on her _____.

8 Have you got a _____ so we can watch this film? We've only got a DVD.

Pronunciation | compound nouns

2 **a** Choose the best word to complete the rule:

In compound nouns, the stress is usually on the *first/second* part. Sometimes it is on both parts.

b 3.2 Listen and mark the stress in these compound nouns. Which three compound nouns have the stress on both parts?

> credit card   table tennis   T-shirt
> science fiction   earring   sunglasses
> traffic lights   mother tongue   parking meter
> dining room   baby-sitter   brother-in-law
> first aid

Grammar | future probability

3 Put the words in the correct order to make sentences.

1 at probably party you 'll the see We.

2 not He want might come to.

3 airport us may They at meet the.

4 call Simmons the Mrs about contract might.

5 for you table eight book, please o'clock Could a ?

6 you buy Do house think you the might ?

7 week I be until next won't probably back .

4 Complete the sentences with verbs from the box.

> won't arrive   might come   could
> 'll probably need   might become
> won't need   may have   'll rain

1 The manager probably _____ until later.

2 I can't find my umbrella. Do you think it _____?

3 **A:** When is Marc coming to see us?
   B: Perhaps this weekend. He _____ on Saturday.

4 Bring the map with you. We _____ it to find their house.

5 I haven't been well recently. I _____ to go to hospital.

6 There is nobody here today. _____ you call back next week?

7 You can take the laptop. I probably _____ it today.

8 He's very good at running. He _____ a professional.

Formal phone calls

5 **a** Delete the extra word in each line of the dialogue.

[1] Good morning. Sonny Korean Banks Ltd. Can I to help you?

☐ Thank you. I'll just put you through. In one moment.

☐ Certainly so.

☐ Yes, this is Jasper Coffin. I'm returning for his call.

☐ Yes, I'd very like to speak to Mr Allen, please.

☐ I'm afraid he's on the other line at the moment. Would you like to call he back later?

☐ May I ask who's calling me, please?

☐ Could he call me at the office, on 0052 427 9835? I'll be here always until seven p.m. Thank you. Goodbye.

☐ Could I to leave a message?

☐ Goodbye.

b Number the lines of the dialogue in the correct order.

c 3.3 Listen and check your answers.

Reading

6 **a** Read the article and match the headings to paragraphs A–D.

How your house will change ☐
Predictions that were wrong ☐
Your clothes will know where you are ☐
Changes in information technology ☐

2020 – how technology will rule our lives

A When Thomas Watson, the founder of IBM, was asked in 1943 how he viewed the future of technology, he famously replied that one day there might be a worldwide market 'for maybe five computers'. H G Wells, on the other hand, predicted in 1901 that the **public transport** of the future would probably consist of a system of moving walkways, where people would step from walkway to walkway to get to their destination.

B Neither of these technological predictions has been very accurate, so what do we think will really change? The answer is probably not that we will have lots of new inventions, but that information technology will transform our day-to-day lives. The big **trend** that is going to change things is the way we transmit information. In other words, by 2020 everything large enough to carry a microchip will probably have one, and from there the possibilities are endless.

C We could have fridges that can read the **use-by date** on the milk, and order more when you need it. We could be sent gas bills that include an electronic **reminder** to pay them. We could wash our clothes in washing machines that contact service engineers when there is a problem. The machine would then automatically arrange a time for the engineer to come after finding a free day in your electronic diary. Even bricks could be fitted with electronic identifiers, so that when an architect walks round a half-finished school or hospital an image of the building appears automatically on his **laptop**.

D We may use other devices which automatically change your mobile phone to different **settings**, depending on whether you are in your work or casual clothing. No more work calls in the pub, and no more football text messages in the middle of business meetings. Does this all sound a bit frightening? Well, don't worry. Just remember that even H G Wells got the future wrong!

b Mark the statements true (T) or false (F) according to the article.

1 Thomas Watson thought that in the future everyone would have computers. ☐
2 In the future more objects will probably carry microchips. ☐
3 Fridges will order your milk. ☐
4 It is possible that the washing machine will fix itself. ☐
5 We might find microchips in the walls of buildings. ☐
6 We will probably have to wear the same clothes at work and when we go out. ☐

c Complete the sentences with the words in **bold** from the article.

1 There is a new _____ in mobile phone ring tones.
2 I need to change the _____ on my phone. It's too quiet.
3 You should check the _____ on that cheese. I bought it three weeks ago!
4 The best thing about living in Lisbon is the _____. It is so easy to get around.
5 We should send them a _____ to pay the bill.
6 I've just bought a new _____. It's much better than my old computer!

Lifestyle

1 Reorder the letters and make words to complete the sentences.

1 She lives in a _____ of flats. (clokb)

2 My apartment is on the fifth _____ and there's no lift. (rolof)

3 It is a residential _____. (eara)

4 My lifestyle is rather _____ at the moment. (techic)

5 Look out of the window. What a fantastic _____! (wiev)

6 They live a long way from the centre, in the _____. (burssub)

7 It's a lovely house, a bit _____. (ldo-saofinehd)

8 There is a park near here, with a _____ for children. (gorlandyup)

9 It's a great city – very _____. (vilely)

10 We go out a lot, because we like _____. (bluncibg)

11 The office is on the _____ of town. (sutsorikt)

12 Shall we have breakfast on the _____? (clanybo)

Present Continuous, *going to/will* for future

2 Correct the mistakes in the following sentences.

1 **A:** Are you going to Spain again this year?
   B: No. We going to Greece instead.

2 I don't think I go to the cinema tonight because I'm too tired.

3 Who is meet us at the airport?

4 We getting married in June.

5 **A:** Have you decided which one you want to buy yet?
   B: Yes. I will to take this one, please.

6 We're going see Andrea tomorrow. Do you want to come with us?

7 **A:** I'm really hungry.
   B: OK. I'm going to make us some lunch now.

8 **A:** What are you doing at the weekend?
   B: We will go to visit my mother-in-law.

9 Do you will come with us to the office?

10 Can you tell Jonathan I see him later?

11 Do you coming to Madrid to watch the football?

12 Sue is leave for Brazil and I'm not going to see her any more.

Comparatives/superlatives/ adjectives for describing places

3 Complete the sentences using comparative/ superlative forms of the adjectives in brackets.

1 I love the Italian countryside. It's even _____ _____ _____ I expected. (picturesque)

2 Rio carnival is fantastic. It's probably _____ _____ carnival in the world. (lively)

3 The tsunami hit some of the _____ _____ beaches in Asia. (unspoilt)

4 The week we spent in a Buddhist temple was probably the _____ _____ week in my life. (peaceful)

5 Those old blocks of flats make the area look _____. (ugly)

6 It's a residential area with nothing to do there. It's _____ _____ part of the city. (dull)

7 I think it would look better if it were _____ _____. (modern)

8 They have stopped cars driving in the centre, so now it is much _____ _____. (polluted)

9 My mother-in-law cleaned the house. It's _____ than it has ever been before! (clean)

10 The town was so busy. It's much _____ _____ than it was a few years ago. (touristy)

Compound nouns

4 The compound nouns are in the wrong sentences. Rewrite the sentences putting the compound nouns in the correct places.

1 I didn't wake up in time because I forgot to set my washing machine.

2 It's cold in here. Let's turn on the air-conditioning.

3 When she opened the door the video recorder went off and soon the police arrived.

4 I left a message on your central heating.

5 I don't have anything to wear because my clothes are all in the alarm clock.

6 Can you set the burglar alarm to record this film at nine o'clock?

7 My new car has mobile phone which I use when it is really hot.

8 Can I borrow your answering machine? I need to call my office.

Future probability

5 Write sentences using the prompts. Include the words in brackets.

1 We/see you/in the restaurant. (probably)
2 Do you think/she/say 'Yes'? (might)
3 I think/I/be late/for the lesson. (going)
4 You/need/to change money. (definitely not)
5 They/ask you/for your passport. (certainly)
6 We/not/get an answer/until tomorrow. (may)
7 I/call her again in the morning. (definitely)
8 She/arrive/at any time. (could)
9 Helga/go/to Russia next year. (probably not)
10 He/accept/the job he was offered. (might not)
11 We/stay/for long. (probably not)
12 I/contact/them/until I know/the answer. (certainly not)

Prefixes and suffixes

6 Use prefixes and suffixes to complete the dialogues.

1 A: How's your new job?
B: Terrible. I'm _____worked and underpaid.
2 A: I haven't seen your girlfriend for a long time. How is she?
B: I don't know. She's my __ – girlfriend now.
3 A: I'm afraid I can't make the meeting tomorrow.
B: That's not a problem. We can ___arrange it.
4 A: Do you get on with your new flat-mate?
B: He's OK, but he's very mess__.
5 A: I paid over £5,000 for the insurance.
B: That's unbeliev_____!
6 A: I love it here. It's so quiet.
B: Yes. It's very peace____.
7 A: Where is Saskia?
B: I don't know. It's ___usual for her to be late.
8 A: This is a table for six people, but we booked for twelve.
B: I think there's been a ___understanding.
9 A: I wrote the song myself.
B: Did you? That's very creat___!
10 A: I can't cut this.
B: Try this knife. This one is use___ for cutting meat.

How to...

7 a Write one or two words from the box to complete each line of the dialogue.

> Could Can about it's put ask
> not call the like leave One

1 Good morning. Casa Bruno. I help you?
2 he call me back? My mobile number is 01797 202345
3 Hello. I'd to speak to Mr Marconi, please.
4 I'll you through. moment.
5 Yes, Gabriella Saltini. I'm calling the new designs.
6 May I who's calling?
7 Can I a message?
8 I'm afraid he's here at the moment. Would you like to back later?
9 Certainly. What's message?

b Put the lines in Ex. 7a in the correct order.

8 Use the prompts in brackets to complete the second sentence so that it means the same as the first.

1 Juan is much taller than Diego.
Diego _____. (as)
2 London is more expensive than New York.
New York _____. (cheap)
3 More tourists visit Glasgow now than they did ten years ago.
Glasgow _____ before. (touristy)
4 I have never seen a city which is more picturesque than Florence.
Florence _____. (most)
5 Los Angeles is more polluted than San Francisco.
San Francisco _____. (not)
6 Most cities are dirtier than Singapore.
Singapore is _____. (one)
7 More things happen in Shanghai nowadays.
Shanghai _____ recently. (busier)
8 The west coast of the island has not had so many visitors.
The west coast _____. (unspoilt)
9 Terrorist activity has meant that life in cities is more dangerous.
Due to terrorist activity, life _____ before. (safe)
10 The old gallery was not as modern as the new one.
The new gallery _____. (modern)

Vocabulary | time and money collocations

1 Cross out the endings which are not possible.

1 Don't go to that film! It's a waste of *time/thought/money*.

2 That man stole my *money/bicycle/time*.

3 Joining a gym is a good way to spend your *time/money/hobby*.

4 She earned *our time/our thanks/lots of money*.

5 I can't go on holiday. I haven't got any *time to spare/money to spare/chance to spare*.

6 Can you lend me *some time/some money/your car?*

Vocabulary | phrasal verbs

2 Complete the paragraph with verbs from the box. Change the tense where necessary.

> break up   pick up   work out   catch up
> run out   end up   drop out

Life-changer: Steve Riddell tells us how a bad time turned good

I was having the worst time of my life. I'd just (1) _____ with my girlfriend and (2) _____ of university. I needed to (3) _____ what I was going to do with the rest of my life. So I went travelling around South America. The idea was to keep travelling until I (4) _____ of money. After a few months I'd (5) _____ some Spanish and made some friends in Colombia. We went our separate ways, but later I decided to (6) _____ with them in Cali. What a fantastic place! I (7) _____ living there for ten years!

3 Correct the mistakes in each of these sentences.

1 Do you know the answer? I can't work it on out.

2 When I was living in Germany I picked some German.

3 I hated university so I dropped it out.

4 I missed some lessons but I caught quickly by working at night.

5 He was a brilliant young scientist and he ended working for the government.

6 Unfortunately, Lisa and I broke it up last week.

7 Oh no! We've run of milk. Can you go and buy some?

Grammar | question tags

4 **a** Complete each sentence with a question tag, then match them to the pictures.

1 You haven't eaten spaghetti before, _____?

2 You haven't used chopsticks before, _____?

3 You didn't revise, _____?

4 You've never played the violin before, _____?

5 You're not nervous, _____?

6 You arrived from Russia, _____?

b Match the questions 1–6 to the answers a–f.

a Yes, I did. It was snowing when I left. ☐

b No, I'm not. I just don't like heights. ☐

c Yes, I did. But I think I'm in the wrong room! ☐

d Yes, I have, but it didn't taste this good. ☐

e No, I haven't. I've always used a fork. ☐

f No, I haven't. But I'm a fast learner. ☐

5 Match the question tags a–l, on the next page, to the sentences 1–12.

1 We're going home now, ☐

2 You'll be back tomorrow, ☐

3 She has eaten already, ☐

4 I'm on the list, ☐

5 You're from Ghana, ☐

6 He won't shoot, ☐

7 They work here, ☐

8 We stayed here before, ☐

9 You eat meat, ☐

10 She plays the guitar, ☐

11 They were in your class, ☐

12 I passed my exam, ☐

a didn't we?
b don't you?
c aren't we?
d will he?
e doesn't she?
f won't you?
g didn't I?
h aren't I?
i aren't you?
j hasn't she?
k don't they?
l weren't they?

Listening

6 **4.1** Nancy Bryant, a fraud prevention officer, is talking about how to stop financial crime. Listen to the recording, then answer the questions below.

> **fraud** (n) an illegal trick intended to deceive another person
>
> **fake** (adj, v, n) make something look like it is real when it is not

1 Listen to Parts 1, 2 and 3. Number these topics in the order Nancy talks about them.
   'phishing' ☐
   features of secure websites ☐
   investing your money ☐
   her job ☐
   Internet fraud ☐
   shopping online ☐

2 Listen to each part separately, then answer the questions.
   Part 1
   1 What does Nancy do in her job?
   2 Why is Internet fraud easier for criminals these days?

   Part 2
   3 What does Nancy say about cheap offers for Internet shoppers?
   4 What two things should you never give over the Internet?

   Part 3
   5 What is phishing?
   6 What two features tell us a website is probably safe?

TAPESCRIPT

Part 1
I: Nancy, fraud is becoming more and more common. Every day we hear of new cases of people losing large amounts of money.
N: That's right.
I: And your job is . . .?
N: My job is to tell the public what's happening, and explain how to stop fraud.
I: The main area you're working on now is Internet fraud. Is that right?
N: That's right. For criminals, Internet fraud is easier because it's so impersonal. In the old days they had to make fake cheques and to be actors. Now they can steal money without ever meeting their victims.

Part 2
I: Nancy, what can we actually do to prevent Internet fraud?
N: Many things. Firstly, be careful about shopping online. If someone offers you something incredibly cheap, then that's a dangerous sign. Or if you see an offer asking you to invest your money now, be careful. Most real investment opportunities don't work like this. They don't come looking for strangers over the Internet.
I: What about giving your details over the net?
N: Never give bank account numbers or passwords over the net.

Part 3
N: There is a trick used by criminals called 'phishing': p, h, i, s, h, i, n, g.
I: Phishing? What's that?
N: It's when you receive an email that says it's from a famous company. The email always says 'Urgent'! And it asks for your details – it asks for your password and other information. And it says, if you don't do this in 24 hours, your account will close. Now, often these emails look very professional. They may have links to real websites. But they are fakes. It's easy to fake a website, easy to steal logos and copy websites. Anyway, of course the victim panics and gives his information and this is where the problem starts.
I: You mention fake websites. If we're shopping online, how do we know the website is secure? How do we know it's safe?
N: Two things. The order form should have the letters 'https' at the top of the screen. The 's' means it's a secure site that hides your information. The second thing is to look for an image of a lock or a key at the bottom of the screen. These usually mean the site is safe.

Vocabulary | personal qualities

1 Write the words in the correct places and find the hidden word.

Hidden word

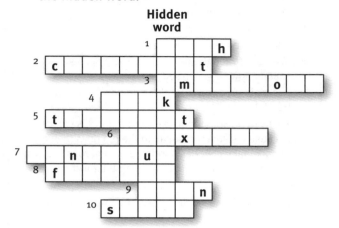

1 Managers have to be good _____ people.

2 She's really _____. She believes in her own ability.

3 He's _____. He plans to be the most famous singer in the world.

4 Politicians have to _____ long hours.

5 Teachers need to be _____ and to respect other people's opinions.

6 Police officers have to be _____ because they work at all hours of the night and day.

7 Our boss is really _____. He's always giving us presents.

8 Financial consultants need to be good with _____.

9 The boss is very _____. He never lets us have a holiday or extra pay.

10 Actors need a good _____ of humour.

Hidden word: All workers should known their strengths and _____.

Grammar | modal verbs

2 Correct the mistakes.

1 You must to come here now.

2 I've finished. What I should do now?

3 You don't must smoke in the office.

4 You haven't to wear a suit, but you can if you want to.

5 Shouldn't you to be at home now?

6 Am I have to buy a ticket?

7 She doesn't have to cleaning her room every day; only at weekends.

8 Our boss have to be in the office at 7.00a.m.

9 I must going to the station now.

10 We are don't have to walk. We can take the car.

3 Read the short texts and choose the correct alternatives.

> Internet use is primarily for study purposes. THIS IS A SILENT AREA.

1 People *shouldn't/don't have to/should* use the Internet mainly for studying.

2 People *don't have to/have to/should* be quiet here.

> Adults and children 12 years and above; take 1 or 2 tablets every 4 hours; WARNING: do not take more than 12 tablets in 24 hours.

3 Adults and children *should/mustn't/can't* take either one or two tablets.

4 Adults and children *mustn't/should/don't* take more than twelve tablets in one day.

> No pets are allowed in student houses. We recommend that students check their mail every day, if possible.

5 Students *have to/don't have to/mustn't* keep pets in the houses.

6 Students *should/have to/mustn't* check their mail every day.

> Free entrance. Children under 8 to be accompanied by an adult.

7 You *have to/shouldn't/don't have* to pay.

8 Children aged eight and older *don't have to/mustn't/have to* go with an adult.

Writing

4 Put the sentences in the correct order to make two letters. The first letter is an invitation. The second letter is the response.

Dear Mr Mishovsky, ☐1

We look forward to hearing from you. ☐

I am afraid I am unable to attend due to a business trip in Switzerland. ☐

Dear Miles Broom, ☐

I have enclosed a form with further information which you can also use to reserve places. ☐

Yours sincerely,

Reuben Mishovsky ☐

I do hope the evening goes well. ☐

I am writing to invite you to our annual dinner in the Atrium Restaurant on 19th July. ☐

Yours sincerely,

Miles Broom ☐

The dinner will begin at 8.00. ☐

Thank you for the invitation to the annual dinner. ☐

Pronunciation

5 **a** 【4.2】 Listen to the sentences below. Mark the two stressed syllables in each sentence.

We mustn't be late.

1 I have to work.
2 We should go to Poland.
3 Do I have to sing?
4 I must get home.
5 You don't have to leave.
6 You shouldn't do that.
7 They mustn't drive there.
8 It doesn't have to be big.

b Listen again and repeat the sentences.

Reading

6 **a** Read the text. Are the sentences below true (T) or false (F)?

1 William Johnstone knew how to buy things over the Internet. ☐
2 The person who was selling the aeroplane sent it to William's home. ☐
3 Bill Davies thought he was going to win a lot of money. ☐
4 Many other people had chosen the same winning numbers as Davies. ☐
5 Ridley Toowomba spent all of his lottery money in two months. ☐
6 Toowomba is sad because he is not rich now. ☐
7 Samantha Brown knew there was some money hidden in the mattress. ☐
8 Mr and Mrs Brown lost £18,000. ☐

b Read the text again and select the best meaning of these words and phrases.

1 *To blow money* means
   A to spend money intelligently.
   B to spend money quickly and foolishly.
2 *Go on a spending spree* means
   A to buy a lot of things very quickly.
   B to have an expensive holiday.
3 *Winnings* means
   A the money you save.
   B prize money.
4 *Jackpot* means
   A a large amount of money that you can win.
   B a pot where you keep money.
5 *In debt* means
   A without a job.
   B you owe (have to pay) money to someone, or to an institution.
6 *Life savings* means
   A money for saving your life (if you have to go to hospital).
   B all the money you have saved.

How not to get rich quick

William Johnstone, aged seven, went on an Internet shopping website, and, using his mother's credit card, bought himself an aeroplane. No, not a toy aeroplane. A jet-fighter. Fortunately, the seller realised there was something wrong when he asked for the delivery address. Flat number 53 in downtown Detroit was not the answer he was expecting. In this case, not a penny was spent, but there are plenty of other cases of people **blowing lots of money** very quickly, very stupidly.

Californian Bill Davies didn't even get that far. When he saw that he had the winning numbers in his local lottery, he immediately ordered a Mercedes, booked a family holiday in Hawaii and had a champagne dinner for friends and family. When he went to pick up his **winnings**, he found that 9,022 others had also won first prize! His share of the **jackpot** was $40.

Ridley Toowomba won nearly $1,000,000 on the lottery in March 2001. By May, he had $400 left. 'I got a bit excited,' said the builder, 24. He **went on a spending spree** and bought six cars, including two for friends. Of those six, by May he had already crashed two, and his friend crashed a third in June. Fortunately, Toowomba was able to return to his old job. 'It was fun while it lasted,' he said, 'but I'm happier working with my mates.'

When 76-year-old Samantha Brown realised her husband was **in debt**, she decided to sell as many things as possible, including an old mattress. A few weeks later her husband nervously asked her where the mattress was. Hidden inside it were his **life savings** of £18,000. They managed to find the mattress but not the money which, strangely, 'had taken a walk'.

Vocabulary | opposites

1 Complete the unfinished words.

Successful (1) ad__ share many common elements. They are clear, honest and informative. They answer the questions: who, what, where, when, why and how? The ad's message usually answers these questions: why will this product (2) <u>succ</u>__ where others (3) <u>fa</u>__ ? Why should (4) <u>buy</u>__ keep returning to this product? People will (5) <u>respo</u>__ to an ad only if they see some kind of (6) <u>rewa</u>__ in it for them. For example, ads often suggest that unless you (7) <u>bu</u>__ this product, you will appear unfashionable. But if you buy it, you will be loved and admired.

2 Choose the best words to complete the sentences.

1 The company *adverts/advertises/consumes* regularly on TV and local radio.

2 The *reward/respond/success* of the project depends on us.

3 We usually *sell/consume/fail* about 4,000 copies of this magazine every month.

4 This *responses/punish/product* is very popular in China.

5 Our business *succeeds/produces/rewards* fifteen types of material for curtains.

6 Drinks companies make some of the best *punishments/buyers/advertisements* on TV.

7 The population *fails/responds/consumes* nearly 100,000 tons of rice every year.

8 When we introduced our new perfume, the public *response/sellers/reward* was fantastic.

9 Our company *rewards/succeeds/fails* the workers' creativity.

10 The average *failure/buyer/advertisement* of our jeans is female and around sixteen years old.

Pronunciation | word stress

3 **a** **4.3** Listen to the recording. Mark the stress on the words in **bold**.

1 It was a great **advertisement**.

2 We'll **advertise** on TV.

3 I complained but they didn't **respond**.

4 She won a **reward**.

5 I feel like a **failure**!

6 I knew you'd **succeed**.

7 Now you're a **success**!

8 What a terrible **punishment**!

b Listen again to check, then listen and repeat.

Grammar | if/when/unless/as soon as/ first conditional

4 Choose the correct alternatives.

1 *As soon as/If* you arrive, will you call me?

2 *If/Unless* you eat better food, you won't get sick.

3 *As soon as/Unless* you work harder, you won't pass the exam.

4 *If/When* you wake up tomorrow, you'll see snow.

5 *As soon as/If* she liked that book, she'll love this one!

6 *If/Unless* we find a taxi right now, we'll miss the plane.

7 *Unless/If* I see Dave, I'll tell him you called.

8 *When/Unless* you go on holiday, will you send me a postcard?

9 *If/Unless* you you take an umbrella, you won't get wet.

10 *When/Unless* you get home we'll watch a DVD.

5 Match the two halves of the sentences, 1–7 to a–g.

1 If the students get under 50 percent in the final exam, ☐

2 We won't give you a refund ☐

3 If you have problems remembering names, ☐

4 Unless you pay for the ticket within four days, ☐

5 We will continue to deliver the magazine ☐

6 The committee will inform you ☐

7 When you subscribe to News24.com, ☐

8 The taxi will pick you up ☐

a as soon as it makes its decision.

b unless you bring the receipt.

c you will benefit from the course in Memory Development.

d we will email you a secret password.

e they won't be able to move to the next level of the class.

f when you finish work.

g our office won't be able to guarantee you a seat.

h unless you tell us that you no longer wish to receive it.

6 Put the verbs in brackets into the correct tense.
Include the pronouns where necessary.

1 **A:** I _____ (not be) home for dinner unless _____ (finish) my work.

  B: As soon as _____ (know) if you're coming, _____ (phone) me?

2 **A:** Where _____ you _____ (go) if you _____ (take) a holiday?

  B: If _____ (have) enough money, I _____ (visit) my aunt in Canada.

3 **A:** When you _____ (graduate), _____ (become) a professor?

  B: If I _____ (find) a job, it _____ (not be) as a professor. I'll be a research assistant first.

4 **A:** We _____ (be) stuck here for hours unless _____ (turn) off the motorway.

  B: If we _____ (not find) a restaurant, we _____ (die) of hunger.

Reading

7 **a** Read the text and tick the best heading.

1 The dangers of advertising ☐
2 Using computers to follow animals ☐
3 The future of the personalised ad ☐

b Which paragraph tells us:

1 what RFID is? ☐
2 about potential problems of RFID? ☐
3 how the future of advertising is seen in a movie? ☐
4 how shops intend to use RFID? ☐
5 how RFID is used now? ☐
6 how government and businesses may use RFID in the future? ☐

c Write T (true) or F (false).

RFID tags are:

1 very small. ☐
2 used for following the movements of animals. ☐
3 used as weapons by the US Department of Defence. ☐
4 in all clothes. ☐
5 used by some commercial companies already. ☐
6 dangerous for the health of workers. ☐

A There's a scene in the film Minority Report which tells us about the future of advertising. Detective John Anderton (played by Tom Cruise) is walking through a shopping mall when the advertisements on the walls start talking to him. They greet him by his name and tell him about the latest products he should buy. How do they know who he is? And how do they know his shopping habits?

B The answer is RFID – radio frequency identification. RFID is in many ways a great idea. How does it work? Tiny computer chips (or 'tags') are attached to objects, clothes or packaging. These chips can be read by a central computer network. If you want to find your lost dog or to research the movements of a herd of elephants, RFID is very helpful. Just put the tag on the animal and watch from a safe distance. RFID has commercial uses too. Delta Airlines uses it to track luggage and the US Department of Defence uses it to count its weapons and vehicles.

C So what's the connection between RFID and advertising? Well, imagine your clothes have an RFID tag. Every time you enter the shopping mall a scanner 'reads' your name, age and buying habits. It knows which shampoo you buy, which bread you prefer, the size of your feet. The scanner then uses this information to target you with special offers. It sounds like science fiction, but some companies already use RFID and a large US supermarket chain plans to use it very soon.

D So, what's the problem? The problem is that great technology is often used for less great purposes. RFID may, in future, be used to track people instead of products. The boss may decide to track his workers – to see who spends their time smoking outside or taking long lunch breaks. The government may decide it wants to see which books you are reading or which political gatherings you attend. As all shoppers know, everything costs something. The cost of RFID may be your privacy.

Question tags

1 What would you say to a friend? Complete the sentences using a question tag. Use the ideas in brackets.

1 The sky is black and it's raining heavily. (horrible day)

It's _____?

2 Your friend is looking thinner than usual. (lose weight)

You've _____?

3 You're listening to a boring radio show. (not very interesting)

This _____?

4 You think your friend secretly ate your last chocolate. (ate)

You _____?

5 You are saying goodbye to a friend who is going travelling. (write to me)

You will _____?

6 You are looking for your sunglasses. (see)

You haven't _____?

7 Your friend is at your barbecue. You think she is a vegetarian. (eat meat)

You don't _____?

8 You are checking that your friend knows how to drive. (can)

You _____?

9 You are talking about your first ever teacher. (wonderful)

She was _____?

10 You check that your friend still runs regularly. (every day)

You still _____?

Question tags and modals of obligation

2 Correct the sentences. Either add a word or cross out a word.

1 We should to bring flowers, shouldn't we?

2 You don't have to freeze this food, you?

3 I need to send Judith an email, I?

4 We mustn't have write in the book, must we?

5 They shouldn't arrive so late, should not they?

6 He has go to class now, doesn't he?

7 She doesn't have to be wear a hat, does she?

8 I must invite Samuel, I?

9 You have to memorise the password, haven't don't you?

10 None of us has should be worried, should we?

Modals of obligation/first conditional

3 Complete the second sentence so that it means the same as the first. Use two to four words.

1 Unless we eat early, there won't be any food left. (If)

_____ eat early, there won't be any food left.

2 Immediately after you arrive, you will receive a ticket. (as)

You will be given a ticket _____ you arrive.

3 It's not necessary for us to book a place on the course. (have)

We _____ book a place on the course.

4 If I drink too much coffee, I'll be awake all night. (be)

_____ able to sleep if I drink too much coffee.

5 It's a good idea to call the office first. (phone)

We _____ the office first.

6 Playing ball games is forbidden here. (mustn't)

You _____ ball games here.

7 She can take the test if she wants to, but it isn't obligatory. (have)

She _____ the test.

8 He won't come to the meeting unless it's really necessary. (come)

He _____ to the meeting if it's really necessary.

9 You should wash your hands before you eat. (eat)

You _____ before washing your hands.

10 When I leave university, I'll go abroad immediately. (soon)

I'll go abroad _____ I leave university.

4 Circle the correct words.

1 Unless we *buy/will buy* a phone card, we *won't/will* be able to call home.

2 *If/As soon as* you don't like meat, you *won't/don't* enjoy this restaurant.

3 When you *will pass/pass* the cinema, you *will to/will* see an Internet cafe. Turn left there.

4 *Will you/You will* call me as soon as you *will know/know* the answer?

5 *Unless/If* they don't take credit cards, we *won't/can't* be able to pay.

6 It *will/doesn't* be great for Europe when these countries *join/will join* the EU.

7 Technology *will/won't* develop if we *put/will put* money into it.

8 *When/If* you reach the age of 17, we *will organise/organise* driving lessons for you.

9 *Unless/When* that bag weighs less than ten kilos, you *won't/will* be able to take it.

10 *Won't you/You won't* fall off your bicycle if you *won't/don't* use your hands?

Phrasal verbs and time/money collocations

5 Cross out the word/phrase that can't follow the phrasal verb.

1 I broke up with *my boyfriend/our relationship/my wife*.

2 They dropped out of *the lesson/college/school*.

3 We had to work out *the answer/what to do/quickly*.

4 I picked up *my errors/many skills/some vocabulary*.

5 We ran out of *time/life/money*.

6 She caught up with *her time/him/her work*.

7 He ended up *working here/in hospital/finally*.

8 I don't get on with *him/my boss/my shoes*.

9 They put up with *the noise/the opportunity/the weather*.

10 They knocked down *the car/the wall/the house*.

Vocabulary

6 Find pairs of opposites in the box. Answer the questions using the words/expressions.

> reward   time to spare   success
> buyer   produce   use money wisely
> not worth the money
> respond to an advertisement
> failure   punishment   seller   consume
> not enough time   advertise   waste money
> good value for money

Who spends money in a shop? A buyer.

1 What do you have if you're early? _____

2 What do you get if you commit a crime? A _____

3 What do you think if something is excellent and cheap? It's _____

4 What do companies do to sell more of their products? _____

5 What do eaters, drinkers and buyers do? _____

6 What do you win if you do something good? A _____

7 What do you have if you or your company does something well? _____

8 What do you think if something is expensive and bad? It's _____

9 What do you do if you spend money on stupid things? _____

10 What do you have if you're in a hurry (in a rush)? _____

Confusing words

7 Which sentence in each pair is correct?

1 A I have an interesting work.
  B I have an interesting job.

2 A Remind me to buy milk tomorrow.
  B Remember me to buy milk tomorrow.

3 A I don't want to lose this show.
  B I don't want to miss this show.

4 A She said me about your problem.
  B She told me about your problem.

5 A Can you lend me some money?
  B Can you borrow me some money?

6 A He robbed a famous museum.
  B He stole a famous museum.

7 A How was your travel?
  B How was your trip?

8 A Skiing is always fun.
  B Skiing is always funny.

9 A Can I rent an umbrella?
  B Can I borrow an umbrella?

10 A He is two metres tall.
   B He is two metres high.

How to ...

8 a Correct the mistakes.

1 I having a party on Friday. ☐

2 Are you like to come? ☐

3 I am writing invite you to the Annual Mason's Ball. ☐

4 I've attach a map, so you can find my place easily! ☐

5 Come any time after during 8.oo. ☐

6 Dinner will be served to at 8.30. ☐

7 I love to come to your party! ☐

8 I will be pleased attend the Choral Society's AGM. ☐

9 Sorry, I don't make it because I've got another party to go to. ☐

10 I am afraid I am unable to attend due for a previous engagement. ☐

b Which sentences are formal (F)? Which are informal (I)? Put F or I in the boxes.

5.1 Spare time

Vocabulary | free time activities

1 Complete the crossword.

Across

1 They are used to protect the hands.
4 Japanese martial art.
5 Indoor racquet game played with a small ball.
6 Exercise class with music.
8 Place where people play tennis.
9 Outdoor activity with flowers!
10 Water sport in which you catch your dinner!
12 Place where people lift weights.

Down

2 Team game with six players and a ball.
3 Someone that plays against you.
5 Sea sport with a board.
7 Sport with bicycles.
11 It's used for separating two volleyball teams.

Grammar: Present Perfect Simple vs Continuous

2 Choose the correct verbs.

1 She's *finished/been finishing* her book. She wrote the final page last night.
2 I've *watched/been watching* this film for an hour now and I don't understand anything!
3 I'm exhausted because I've *worked/been working* since 5a.m.
4 We've *gone/been going* to samba classes since June. It's fun. Why don't you come?
5 How long have you *known/been knowing* Clara?
6 Your tennis is getting better. Have you *practised/been practising*?
7 That was the best film I've ever *seen/been seeing*.

3 Use the prompts to complete the dialogues. Use the Present Perfect Simple or Continuous. Write two, three or four words in each space.

1 A: I met Ravi ten years ago.
   B: So you _____ Ravi for ten years. (know)
2 A: Can't you find your glasses?
   B: No. I _____ them for hours. (look for)
3 A: You look tired.
   B: I _____ since eight in the morning. (run)
4 A: Where have you been?
   B: I _____ on my computer in my room. (play)
5 A: Do you like my new CD?
   B: I _____ it yet, so I don't know. (hear)
6 A: She's got a driving lesson tomorrow.
   B: How long _____ to drive? (learn)
7 A: I'm having a party tomorrow.
   B: How many people _____? (invite)

Pronunciation | contractions

4 **5.1** Listen and tick the sentences you hear.

1 A John's been working. ☐
  B John's working. ☐
2 A Have you been eating? ☐
  B Have you eaten? ☐
3 A I've painted it. ☐ B I painted it. ☐
4 A I've been reading. ☐ B I'm reading. ☐
5 A We lost. ☐ B We've lost. ☐
6 A She's finished. ☐
  B She hasn't finished. ☐
7 A Are you seeing her? ☐
  B Have you seen her? ☐
8 A I've done the work. ☐
  B I haven't done the work. ☐

How to ...

5 Choose the best response.

1 A: What shall we do tonight?
   B: *Or we could do this./Why don't we go to the cinema?*
2 A: I think Kew is the nicest place in London.
   B: *I'm not sure about that./Shall we try these?*
3 A: The problem with that restaurant is that it's expensive.
   B: *That's a good idea./So wouldn't it be better to eat at home?*
4 A: Does anyone have any ideas about what to do today?
   B: *Let's go with that./Shall we try a museum?*

Reading and listening

6 `5.2` Read and listen to the story. Then answer the questions.

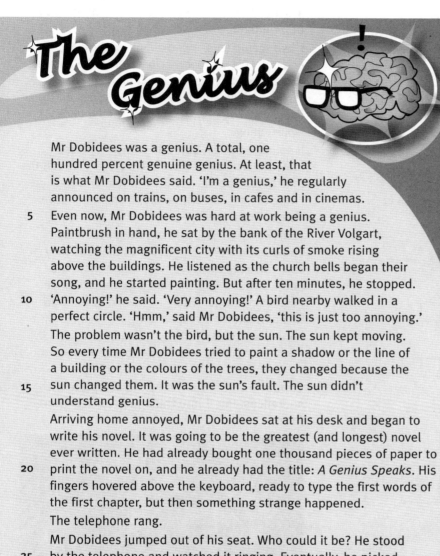

Mr Dobidees was a genius. A total, one hundred percent genuine genius. At least, that is what Mr Dobidees said. 'I'm a genius,' he regularly announced on trains, on buses, in cafes and in cinemas.

5 Even now, Mr Dobidees was hard at work being a genius. Paintbrush in hand, he sat by the bank of the River Volgart, watching the magnificent city with its curls of smoke rising above the buildings. He listened as the church bells began their song, and he started painting. But after ten minutes, he stopped.

10 'Annoying!' he said. 'Very annoying!' A bird nearby walked in a perfect circle. 'Hmm,' said Mr Dobidees, 'this is just too annoying.' The problem wasn't the bird, but the sun. The sun kept moving. So every time Mr Dobidees tried to paint a shadow or the line of a building or the colours of the trees, they changed because the

15 sun changed them. It was the sun's fault. The sun didn't understand genius. Arriving home annoyed, Mr Dobidees sat at his desk and began to write his novel. It was going to be the greatest (and longest) novel ever written. He had already bought one thousand pieces of paper to

20 print the novel on, and he already had the title: *A Genius Speaks*. His fingers hovered above the keyboard, ready to type the first words of the first chapter, but then something strange happened. The telephone rang. Mr Dobidees jumped out of his seat. Who could it be? He stood

25 by the telephone and watched it ringing. Eventually, he picked it up. Silence. No one there. He sat down again. But by now his concentration was gone. Geniuses and telephones should never be in the same room, he decided, so he got up and went to his music room.

30 The music room wasn't really a music room at all. It was a large white space with a piano in the centre. Mr Dobidees sat at the piano, and a list went through his head: Beethoven, Mozart, Bach, Tchaikovsky, Dobidees. 'This is the moment the world has been waiting for,' he said to himself. He breathed deeply. He raised his hands. But just

35 before he could begin, a noise stopped him. A noise from inside himself. He froze. What was it? It happened again. His stomach was making noises! 'This is extremely unusual,' he said. 'Unusual,' he repeated. And he kept repeating it all the way to the supermarket, where he bought a loaf of bread, a packet of cheese, eight onions,

40 a banana and three tomatoes. When he got home he was hungry. After eating some food washed down with a good hot cup of tea, he said to himself, 'I'm a genius. Genius. Me. Dobidees. Genius.' Outside, a dog barked. A cat slept. The annoying sun shone. The world kept turning.

a Write T (true) or F (false).

1 Mr Dobidees believes he is a genius. ☐

2 He couldn't paint the city because of a bird. ☐

3 He has written one thousand pages of a novel. ☐

4 He had a phone conversation. ☐

5 He thinks he will be a great composer. ☐

6 He went shopping because he was hungry. ☐

b Find words in the story that mean:

1 said in public (v) _____

2 the edge of a river (n) _____

3 very impressive (adj) _____

4 floated in the air (v) _____

5 stopped moving completely (v) _____

6 noise made by a dog (v) _____

c What do the following words refer to?

1 Line 07: *its*
   A the city's
   B Mr Dobidees's
   C the River Volgart's

2 Line 14: *they*
   A Mr Dobidees
   B the sun and the bird
   C a shadow or the line of a building or the colours of the trees

3 Line 18: *It*
   A his desk   B his novel
   C paper

4 Line 25: *it*
   A his seat   B the novel
   C the telephone

5 Line 30: *It*
   A the piano   B the music room
   C his concentration

6 Line 36: *it*
   A a noise   B the moment the world had been waiting for
   C his stomach

7 Line 38: *it*
   A his stomach
   B the supermarket
   C 'Unusual'

Vocabulary | books and films

1 **a** Find the key word.

1 When actors are given voices in a foreign language, the film is _____ .

2 A film that follows the original film, using the same characters.

3 A manuscript is made into a book when it is _____.

4 A section of a novel.

5 The main character or famous actor in a film.

6 The name (of a book or film).

7 The story.

8 The film _____ is the place where the film is made.

9 The author of a play is the play's _____.

10 An actor always tries to give a great _____.

11 Music for a film.

key word

```
              1 ☐☐☐☐☐☐☐
        2 ☐☐☐☐☐☐☐☐
    3 ☐☐☐☐☐☐
              4 ☐☐☐☐☐☐☐☐
        5 ☐☐☐☐
            6 ☐☐☐☐
              7 ☐☐☐☐☐☐
          8 ☐☐☐☐☐☐☐☐
          9 ☐☐☐☐☐
      10 ☐☐☐☐☐☐☐☐☐☐
      11 ☐☐☐☐☐☐☐☐☐
```

b The key word is _____ .

Pronunciation | /æ/ /e/ /ɑː/ sounds

2 **a** <u>Underline</u> the two words which have the same vowel sound.

A <u>*when*</u> B *shark* C <u>*bread*</u> D *back*

1 A bag   B tan   C car   D red

2 A hard   B head   C sad   D bed

3 A said   B had   C dead   D star

4 A mad   B heart   C ten   D card

5 A far   B rang   C rat   D ready

6 A start   B pet   C park   D back

b **5.3** Listen to the recording to check your answers.

Grammar | gerunds vs infinitives

3 Jenny Schubert, a book editor, describes her job. Put the verbs in the correct form: gerund or infinitive.

I love *seeing* (see) a book begin to develop, and I try (1)_____ (work) closely with the author. During the early stages, I invite the author (2)_____ (have) dinner with me at home. We usually manage (3)_____ (discuss) the book while eating.

It sounds strange, but I'd like (4)_____ (read) more for pleasure. I don't seem (5)_____ (find) the time to read books outside my field of work, and I hate (6)_____ (start) books when I don't have time to finish them.

I enjoy (7)_____ (speak) to young writers and I advise them (8)_____ (read) as much as they can. I also tell them (9)_____ (write) from the heart, about things that are important to them. I sometimes agree (10)_____ (look) at the work of a new author if I expect (11)_____ (enjoy) the book, but I refuse (12)_____ (read) new work if it's full of spelling mistakes or badly-presented.

4 Choose a verb from the box to complete the sentences. Put it into the infinitive or gerund form.

play (x2)   be   have   study   beat   paint   write

What do the stars do in their free time?

1 Bill Clinton adores _____ the saxophone.

2 Madonna enjoys _____ books for children.

3 Paul McCartney tries _____ regularly and has had exhibitions of his paintings.

4 Robbie Williams is often invited _____ football in celebrity matches.

5 Gisele Bundchen loves volleyball and wanted _____ a professional player.

6 Kylie Minogue loves Scrabble and regularly manages _____ writer, Salman Rushdie!

7 Serena Williams designs clothes and would like _____ her own fashion company.

8 Angelina Jolie finished _____ to be a pilot in 2004. She now flies her own plane.

How to ... | describe a film or book

5 Complete the short reviews using the words in the box.

> recommend   about   act   characters
> plot   sequel   stars   set   thing   by

My favourite book is <u>The Little Prince</u>. The main
(1)_____ are the little prince and the pilot. It was
written (2)_____ de Saint-Exupéry. I really like
it because it talks (3)_____ human relationships.
William, 15

This film is (4)____ in Alcatraz. It's about an
impossible escape from the prison. It (5)____ Nicolas
Cage and Sean Connery, and it was directed by Michael
Bay. The acting was excellent, and another (6)____
I liked was the soundtrack.
Alexandra, 35

The film we saw yesterday, <u>I Robot</u>, is about
robots who (7)_____ like humans. I really liked
it because the (8)_____ was excellent, a really
interesting story. I would (9)_____ this movie to
all my friends. I hope there's a (10)_____.
Akiko, 29

Listening

6 **5.4** Listen to four conversations comparing films and comic books. Complete the notes in the table.

Speaker	Title of film/ comic book	Opinion
1 Denise	*X-Men*	The film was _____ than the comic book. She loved the _____.
2 Ahmed	_____	He preferred the _____. The star looked too _____.
3 Eliza	*Batman*	The comic is dark but the film is _____. She loved the performance of _____.
4 Glynn	_____	He likes the comic and the film. He also loves the _____. He doesn't like _____ as much.

TAPESCRIPT

1

Denise: I've recently seen the *X-Men* film, which I really liked.

Interviewer: Oh yes? What did you like about it?

Denise: I thought it was much better than the comic book. I loved the action.

2

Ahmed: Um ... I saw *Spiderman*. But I didn't like it that much.

Interviewer: Did you prefer the comic?

Ahmed: Yeah, I much preferred the comic to the film. In the comic, the characters are more real, whereas ... um ... in the film, I didn't really like the actor who played Spiderman, the star ... what's his name ... is it Toby Maguire?

Interviewer: Toby Maguire, I think, yes.

Ahmed: He looked too young.

3

Interviewer: You saw *Batman*, didn't you?

Eliza: *Batman, the movie?* I loved it.

Interviewer: Really? More than the comic?

Eliza: The comic is ... like ... really dark, set in this dark city, and it's all really tragic and everything, but the film is kind of funny. And I just loved Jack Nicholson's performance as the Joker.

4

Glynn: I think both the *Superman* comic book and the film were great.

Interviewer: Yeah, me too.

Glynn: And I love the soundtrack.

Interviewer: Yeah, it's great, isn't it?

Glynn: It's one of the things I remember most about the film, actually. Y'know, that music when he's flying above the city.

Interviewer: Yeah.

Glynn: The sequels aren't so good, but the first film's a classic.

Vocabulary | food and eating out

1 a Find ten words connected with food and eating out.

d	e	s	s	e	r	t	l
b	d	t	p	l	a	t	e
o	n	a	p	k	i	n	g
w	h	r	c	u	p	k	l
l	c	t	i	p	b	n	a
s	g	e	m	e	a	l	s
s	e	r	v	i	c	e	s

b Use the words to complete the sentences.

Is there a <u>napkin</u>? I've spilt my drink.
There's one next to your <u>plate</u>.

1 Would you like a _____ of coffee?
2 Is _____ included in the bill?
3 Are you having a _____? There's soup or paté.
4 Did you enjoy your _____?

a No, it isn't. Let's leave the waiter a _____.
b No, I never drink it. But I'll have another _____ of wine, please.
c Well, the main course was delicious, but the _____ was too sweet.
d Yes, I'll have a _____ of soup, please.

c Now pair the questions, 1–4, with the responses, a–d.

1 ☐   2 ☐   3 ☐   4 ☐

Writing | a summary

2 Read the summary of the film *Chocolat*. Put the linking words and the non-defining relative clauses in the correct places in the text.

> after   when   eventually   while

> which is based on Joanne Harris's novel
> which is delicious   who is six years old

A woman and her daughter, (1)_____, arrive in a small French village. (2)_____ the woman opens a chocolate shop opposite the church, the villagers are shocked. But (3)_____ trying her chocolate, (4)_____, they begin to like her. The chocolate brings fun and romance to the village, and (5)_____ the woman is accepted by the community. The film, (6)_____, is very enjoyable. (7)_____ Juliette Binoche is excellent as the chocolate shop owner, Johnny Depp's performance as a wandering romantic steals the film.

Grammar | countable vs uncountable

3 Choose the correct words from the options below.

How to make aubergine bake

This is a simple, delicious dish which doesn't take (1)_____ preparation. You need 2 large aubergines, 4 tomatoes, 2 onions, 1 green pepper, garlic, 2 boiled eggs, cheese, and salt.

Cut the aubergines into slices and leave them in salty water for 20 minutes. Slice the tomatoes, onions, green pepper and eggs. Grate the cheese.

Take a large tray and spread (2)_____ butter on it. Place (3)_____ pieces of aubergine on the tray, add (4)_____ garlic, and (5)_____ little bit of salt. Next, add the tomatoes, onions, pepper and (6)_____cheese.

Repeat the steps adding another layer of the same ingredients. Put the sliced egg on top with (7)_____ pepper. Add (8)_____ of cheese this time and a couple of spoonfuls of oregano. Bake for 30 minutes.

1 **A** a **B** a lot **C** much **D** many
2 **A** some **B** a **C** much **D** many
3 **A** much **B** few **C** a **D** a few
4 **A** a **B** lots of **C** much **D** a few
5 **A** – **B** a **C** the **D** some
6 **A** a **B** much **C** some **D** lot of
7 **A** some **B** few **C** little **D** lots
8 **A** little **B** many **C** some **D** lots

4 Circle the words in each line which are not possible.

1 *a/many/a bar* of chocolate
2 *a piece/bit/couple* of news
3 *a box/few/packet* of sweets
4 *a loaf/lot/little* of bread
5 *some/piece of/many of* advice
6 *not much/a piece of/some* money
7 *a bowl of/few/little* soup
8 *a kilo of/little/few* apples

How to ... | recommend a restaurant

5 Put the words in order to complete the dialogue.

A: Where's that new restaurant, *Mangetout*?

B: the it's square near main (1)_____

A: What type of food does it serve?

B: in specialises food Thai it (2)_____

A: Is the food good?

B: fresh yes, very it's (3)_____

A: What about the service?

B: friendly very waiters the are (4)_____

A: My friend told me that a meal takes hours to arrive!

B: service slow is the a yes, little (5)_____

A: Are the prices reasonable?

B: quite it expensive is (6)_____

A: Would you recommend it?

B: visit a worth it's (7)_____

Reading | a restaurant review

6 **a** Read the descriptions of some people. Then read the restaurant reviews. Who should eat at which restaurant?

1 Brett and Matthew like hot, spicy dishes. They have travelled a lot, and they love South American or Asian food. ☐

2 **The Wilkinsons like cheap, fast food. American food in particular.** ☐

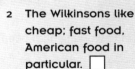

3 Mr and Mrs Lewsey like expensive European food and excellent wine. They want to go to a quiet, comfortable restaurant not too far from the town centre. ☐

4 *Dave and Jessie live on the coast. They are vegetarians, but they sometimes eat fish. They like cheap, cheerful restaurants.* ☐

A Cucina Romana is a modern restaurant specialising in pasta and pizza. Prices vary from £5.00 for our oven-baked calzone to £14.50 for our Seafood Deluxe pasta with shrimp and lobster. Free parking. Wheelchair access. Open daily 1.00 p.m. until midnight.

B Come and get it at MacBurgles Rapido! Hamburger, chips and fizzy drink for just £2.99. Family packs for just £8.99. If you have to wait more than ten minutes, we give you a free meal! Over the Christmas period, book our special Party Room for kids. Call 0207 676 2919 for bookings.

C Taste of the Taj Indian restaurant. Central London. Curries, chicken tikka masala. Excellent quality using fresh herbs and spices. Recommended by the Orion Food Guide: 'An outstanding eating experience.'

D Fisherman's Wharf is a friendly fish restaurant situated at the harbour, just twenty minutes from the centre of Hoban. Serving a wide variety of fish, we can guarantee freshness. All fish are caught locally. On Sundays try our special Seafood Combo of prawns, cod and squid for an unforgettable meal, at just £3.50.

'Fisherman's Wharf is fantastic value.' (Hoban Enquirer)

'Great service, great food!' (City Entertainment Guide, January 2005)

E Bistro Moderne This elegant, exclusive restaurant serves French, Spanish and Italian food. Our extensive cellar has over 400 wines for you to choose from. Prices from £70.00 per person. Open Monday to Saturday 7.00 – 11.30.

b Which restaurants:

1 tell you where they are? ☐ and ☐
2 offer special deals? ☐ and ☐
3 tell you when they are open? ☐ and ☐
4 tell you who has recommended them? ☐ and ☐
5 serve seafood? ☐ and ☐
6 serve meals for under £4.00? ☐ and ☐

5 Megan and Sian like Italian food. The restaurant must be easy to reach and near the centre of the city. They like eating out on Sundays. ☐

Present Perfect Simple and Continuous

1 Put the verbs into the correct form, Present Perfect Simple or Continuous.

1. _____ (you not finish) your work yet? You're really slow!
2. There's chocolate all over your mouth! _____ (you eat) sweets again?!
3. You look bored. _____ (you read) that book about nuclear physics? It's very long, isn't it?
4. I _____ (ask) her for my book six times, and she still hasn't returned it.
5. I'm exhausted. I _____ (study) all night and I still have to do one more essay!
6. It's cold in here because the window _____ (be) open all day.
7. The children are really tired. They _____ (ski) all morning.
8. We _____ (stop) going to yoga classes. It was too stressful!
9. There it is! I _____ (look) for that book for three weeks!
10. There's no paint left. We _____ (use) it all on the wall.

Verb patterns and countable/uncountable nouns

2 Make the correct form of the verbs in brackets (gerund or infinitive) and choose the correct word in *italics*.

1. I enjoy _____ (cook) and I always use *few/a lot/a lot of* garlic.
2. I didn't manage _____ (find out) anything. Did you find *any/many/a lot* information?
3. She really wants _____ (talk) to you. She needs *some/an/a few* advice.
4. I'm looking forward to _____ (meet) you. I've heard *a couple/so much/so many* good things about you.
5. There's something I'd like _____ (tell) you! It's *a/–/a few* good news.
6. They invited us _____ (go) on holiday with them, but it cost *too lot/too many/too much* money.
7. She finished _____ (write) the book years ago, but it took *few/many/much* years to find a publisher.
8. We don't mind _____ (look after) Sammy. Does he like *a/–/little* chocolate?
9. I can't stand _____ (run). It's even worse in *a/too/–* bad weather.
10. He refused _____ (eat) his vegetables. He wanted *an/few/little* ice cream instead!

Verb patterns

3 Cross out the sentence endings which are not possible.

1. I began   A to cry   B playing the violin   C play tennis.
2. I'd like   A a coffee, please   B going home now   C to find a new job.
3. She tried   A writing down new words   B to swim   C bake a cake.
4. We expect   A make some money   B good weather   C to be there at 6.00.
5. Don't forget   A me   B buy milk   C to clean the car.
6. We agreed   A to start at 4.15   B with the doctor   C working together.
7. I stopped   A to have a drink   B play with the dog   C writing poems years ago.
8. He remembered   A dance all night   B meeting you last year   C to bring the presents.
9. She can't stand   A watching TV   B do exercise   C vegetables.
10. Last year the team started   A become popular   B winning   C to attract support.

Present Perfect Simple and Continuous, and countable/uncountable nouns

4 Put the words in order to make sentences.

1. a she's subject years for studying the of been couple.
   _____
2. of heard Mark lot I've interesting a about stories.
   _____
3. haven't enough of some working hard been you.
   _____
4. I've for coming been here years many.
   _____
5. time in spent hasn't Brazil much he.
   _____
6. Prague of us a stayed few before in have.
   _____
7. days been she's taking many work off too.
   _____
8. some to he's find information trying been.
   _____
9. days haven't I for few seen you a.
   _____
10. doing has of my today been mother lot gardening a.
    _____

Vocabulary

5 Write a word from Unit 5 which matches the definition.

- activity to keep the body flexible; sometimes uses music: *a*_____
- type of plate usually used for dessert or soup: *b*_____
- section of a book: *c*_____
- put into another language (a film): *d*_____
- general word for physical activity that is good for your body: *e*_____
- outdoor hobby done next to water; you can eat the result!: *f*_____
- activity in which you grow flowers, plant trees, etc.: *g*_____
- not soft: *h*_____
- a coach/teacher, e.g. for skiing: *i*_____
- slow running: *j*_____
- Japanese martial art: *k*_____
- not heavy or dark: *l*_____
- most important person in a book or film (two words): *m*_____
- something you use while eating, to clean away food: *n*_____
- the person you play against in any sport/game: *o*_____
- story in a film or book: *p*_____
- fairly, but not very: *q*_____
- not smooth: *r*_____
- you eat this before the main course: *s*_____
- money you give for good service: *t*_____
- type of noun which you can't count e.g. water, news, advice, information: *u*_____
- ball sport that uses a net and can be played on the beach: *v*_____
- not narrow: *w*_____

Explaining what you mean

6 **a** Correct the sentences.

1 It's a type machine you use for cooking things fast.
2 It's kind of game that uses pieces like kings and queens.
3 It's the stuffing you find on the ground after a freezing night.
4 It's something you use for boil water to make coffee.
5 They are made by rubber and you put them on your wheels.
6 They are usually rectangle and you put pictures inside them.
7 It's a cold place that is absolutely hug.

8 It's a stick type of tape that you can use to attach paper to a wall.
9 It's a square, hardly type of bread that you can eat with cheese.
10 You use this to wash yourself and smell good. It's very smoothy.

b Match the definitions with the things they describe from Ex. 6a.

noun	definition
a cracker	1
b car tyres	2
c kettle	3
d sellotape	4
e frame	5
f Siberia	6
g ice	7
h soap	8
i microwave	9
j chess	10

How to ...

7 **a** The sentences each have a word missing. Complete the sentences using words from the box.

> prepared   characters   set   visit   in
> improved   worth   a   been   by   it   prices

1 The service is little slow. ☐
2 The main are really interesting. ☐
3 It was directed Francis Ford Coppola. ☐
4 It's worth a. ☐
5 Wouldn't be better to practise every day? ☐
6 I've doing this for about six years. ☐
7 The food is beautifully. ☐
8 It's in Chicago in the 1920s. ☐
9 The are reasonable. ☐
10 It's not really seeing. ☐
11 I've a lot since I first started. ☐
12 It specialises modern French cuisine. ☐

b What do the sentences refer to: a film (F), a restaurant (R) or a hobby (H)? Put the letters in the boxes.

Vocabulary | travel

1 Choose the best words to complete the sentences.

1 I love *going/seeing/having* abroad.
2 Sydney Opera House is Australia's most famous *experience/tour guide/landmark*.
3 The world's largest tropical *jungle/wood/rainforest* is in the Amazon, South America.
4 For a good holiday, I like lying on a *rock/sandy/sand* beach.
5 Prague is one of Europe's great *sensation/historic/history* capitals.
6 We had a truly *forgetful/forgotten/unforgettable* journey around Russia.
7 Rome is full of monuments and museums. It's a great place to *go/have/make* sightseeing.
8 There are many *pack/packing/package* holidays to Thailand, South-east Asia's number one holiday destination.
9 Sun, sea and sand make Majorca the perfect place to have *funny/fun/enjoy* on holiday.
10 If you want to see Egypt's *localised/local/home* culture, go to the market, Khan El Khalili.

Reading | Past Perfect

2 Underline examples of the Past Perfect in the sentences below then put the sentences in the correct places in the text.

1 By now I had finished four, and this was the fifth and last.
2 He had run out of film.
3 We had never expected such silence from a place so large.
4 Had it been like this at the beginning of time, before man existed?

Fish River Canyon is the second biggest canyon in the world. Seeing it was a humbling experience. Apart from its size, the greatest thing about it was its quietness. (a)

What is a canyon? It's nothing but a hole in the ground. But as we stood there, on its edge, we looked down and we could see birds flying below us, and small dried-up rivers 100 feet down, winding their way between the trees. And a thought came to me. (b)

I took out my notebook, as always. (c) Daniel went back to the car to get his camera. But when he returned there was a look on his face which said, 'Disaster!' We were in a beautiful, peaceful place. The sun was going down behind us like a ball of fire dropping into water. It was perfect. 'What's the matter?' I asked. (d)

Grammar | Past Perfect vs Past Simple

3 Write answers using the prompts. Use the Past Perfect positive or negative.

Why did Jack decide to go on holiday? (win)
Because he <u>had won</u> some money.

1 Why was Jack late to check in? (forget)
2 Why did they stop Jack at customs? (pack)
3 Why did Jack smoke in the wrong place in the airport? (see)
4 Why did Jack have problems at the hotel? (book)
5 Why did Jack get sunburnt on the beach? (put on)
6 Why didn't Jack take any photos? (bring)
7 Why couldn't Jack get back into his hotel room one night? (lose)
8 Why was Jack happy to be home? (miss)

How to ... | describe a photo

4 Read what Chee Yun says about her holiday photos. Complete the sentences with the words from the box.

> been   one   shows   afterwards   excited   foreground   on

This photo (1)_____ the Iguaçu Falls. The Falls are on the border of Brazil, Paraguay and Argentina. You can see the two guys we met in the (2)_____ .

This (3)_____ is of the carnival in Recifé. You can see the floats, those big open buses full of people in costumes, (4)_____ the right.

I love this photo. We were really (5)_____ because we were on Sugar Loaf Mountain in Rio for the first time. We had (6)_____ on the chairlift, it was fantastic! (7)_____, we went for a big meal in a restaurant.

Listening

5 **a** Match the halves of the collocations.

1	tour _____	a	the world
2	swim _____	b	animals
3	cheap _____	c	guide
4	all over _____	d	flights
5	greatest _____	e	in the sea
6	get _____	f	challenge
7	wild _____	g	lost

b You will listen to an interview with Melissa who is a travel journalist. What do you think Melissa will talk about?

a   her favourite trip

b   advice for people who want to be travel writers

c   equipment she uses

d   how tourism has changed

e   how long she has been a travel writer

c [6.1] Cover the tapescript. Listen and tick the things Melissa mentions.

d Listen again and answer the questions.

1   How does Melissa feel about her travels?

2   When did she become a travel writer?

3   What is the 'good thing' about modern travel?

4   How has climbing Mount Everest changed?

5   Why does she mention Sandy Hill Pitman?

6   What two pieces of advice does she give to young travel writers?

TAPESCRIPT

I: Melissa, you've travelled to over sixty countries, published eighteen books of travel journalism, got lost in deserts, swum in five seas, been attacked by wild animals, but in a recent interview you say that your journey has only just begun.

M: I feel that way, yes. I think, as you see more, you realise there's more to see. You visit, say, East India, and then you realise you don't know much about the area. And then you want to go to Nepal and Tibet. So, yes, I do feel I'm just starting.

I: How many years have you been a travel writer?

M: A long time, more than thirty years.

I: What changes have you seen in travel and tourism?

M: Well, many. I think these new airlines that offer cheap flights all over the world have made a big difference. People – not necessarily rich people – can now see more of the world, and I think that's a good thing.

I: And there's a bad side too?

M: Of course. I think, well, just as an example: Mount Everest. Mount Everest used to be probably the greatest challenge for any traveller. Well, now it's full of tourists. Tour guides can take you up the mountain and you don't need any training because the guides do everything for you. There was the case of Sandy Hill Pitman in 1996. Her guides carried her laptop computer, coffee machine and luxury food up Everest. She even had fashion magazines delivered to the mountain. Now, for me, that's the bad side of modern tourism. You lose some of the mystery.

I: Melissa, is there any advice you would give to young people who want to be travel writers?

M: Yes, I think the first thing is that you have to make time to write. Wherever you are – in a desert, on a boat, at the top of a mountain. You have to find the time. And if you do it every day, it becomes a habit. The second thing is details. You must look for details. It's no good writing 'The sunset was beautiful'. You have to say exactly what colours you saw, how the colours were reflected in the trees and water. How the sun felt on your face. You have to be very detailed and look more deeply than most people.

Vocabulary | places to visit in a city

1 **a** Find eleven places to visit in a city. The words can go across or down. The first has been done for you.

a	r	t	g	a	l	l	e	r	y
j	d	f	c	a	s	t	l	e	f
m	u	s	e	u	m	f	p	c	o
a	s	h	o	p	s	g	a	h	u
r	s	e	c	a	x	l	r	u	n
k	l	e	s	l	v	a	k	r	t
e	c	u	f	a	t	k	m	c	a
t	a	d	t	c	r	e	o	h	i
c	a	t	h	e	d	r	a	l	n

b Which two places might you visit:

1 for religious reasons? _____ _____
2 to see paintings and sculptures? _____ _____
3 to buy things? _____ _____
4 to see water? _____ _____
5 to see where royal families live? _____ _____

Pronunciation | how to sound polite

2 **6.2** Do the speakers sound polite (P) or impolite (I)? Listen and write P or I in the boxes.

1 Two return tickets to London, please. ☐
2 Where's the bank? ☐
3 Is there a chemist near here? ☐
4 Give me a black coffee. ☐
5 What time does the museum close? ☐
6 Can I get a student discount? ☐
7 I'd like to cash these traveller's cheques, please. ☐
8 I want to see the menu. ☐

How to ... | get around a new place

3 Put the words in the correct order to make questions.

1 city how a much the ticket to centre is ?
2 time what the close palace does ?
3 where you is know do the excuse museum me , ?
4 the , please me the you way to tell can cathedral ?
5 there bank near excuse here is me , a ?
6 to bus go this gallery the art does ?

Grammar | uses of *like*

4 Correct the errors in the sentences. Use *like* in the first sentence of each pair.

1 How's the flat like? Is it big?
2 Do you like some help? I'm free at the moment.
3 Your house is look like a museum. I love your old furniture.
4 I like listen to music. My favourite band is The Fugees.
5 What is your girlfriend look like? Is she tall and blonde? I think I saw her yesterday.
6 What's that film likes? I've heard it's very sad.
7 What would you like do this evening? There's a good film on at the cinema.
8 What did the weather like? I hope it didn't rain and ruin your holiday.

5 Write a question for each answer. Use *like*.

1 A: What _____ he _____ ?
   B: He's intelligent and funny.
2 A: _____ John _____ Pete?
   B: Yes, they look exactly the same!
3 A: _____ you _____ maths?
   B: No, I hate it. I prefer arts subjects.
4 A: What _____ the building _____?
   B: It's quite small, and it has a wooden door and white walls.
5 A: What _____ the concert _____?
   B: It was fantastic! I loved it.
6 A: _____ your mother _____ you?
   B: No, she is much taller and prettier.
7 A: _____ you _____ a cup of tea?
   B: Yes, please.
8 A: What is the weather _____ tomorrow?
   B: I've heard it's going to rain.

Writing | a quick guide

6 Put the words in the correct order.

1 place first Street the go is Princes to
2 the visit Art art of galleries best one the Modern is Museum to
3 Castle mustn't you Edinburgh miss
4 Bannerman's Restaurant make you trip if sure traditional enjoy you include a to food,
5 leave don't without The Grassmarket seeing
6 try why haggis not finally, some ?

Reading

7 **a** Which of these places are shown in the photos?

   a The Sahara Desert

   b Tornado Alley, USA

   c Rainforest, Papua New Guinea

   d Florida Keys, USA

   e Bhutan

  b Which of these places do you think has:

   1 dangerous weather? _____

   2 a peaceful lifestyle? _____

   3 killer sharks? _____

   4 ancient tribes? _____

   5 lots of space? _____

  Now read the text to check your answers.

  c Choose A or B.

   1 Why pay $8,000 to go to Papua? Because

     A you want to see some ancient tribes in the rainforest.

     B you want to live in the rainforest.

   2 Why do you have to dive? Because

     A it's the only way to enter the underwater hotel.

     B you want to touch big, dangerous fish.

   3 Why go to the Sahara? Because

     A you need to get your visa there.

     B it's big and peaceful.

   4 Why go to Roswell? Because

     A you're interested in UFOs and aliens.

     B no one has been there since 1947.

   5 Why might a cow land on your head? Because

     A there are strong tornadoes in mid-west America.

     B there are no more flying fish in the USA.

Out and about on Planet Earth
Where on earth can I ...?

1 See some crazy weather?
Talking of strange things falling out of the sky, one day in 1956 in Uniontown, Alabama, USA, it rained fish. Yes, thousands of fish fell from the sky into the town. If you don't want a fish to land on your head, how about a cow instead? Go to Tornado Alley, in mid-west America. It can get winds strong enough to carry cows, or even houses and trees, for kilometres.

2 Meet aliens?
Go to the International UFO Museum and Research Center, in Roswell, USA. Something strange fell out of the sky in 1947, and people have been going there ever since. Don't expect to see any little green men, though: there aren't any!

3 Find some peace and quiet?
Go to Bhutan, known for its peaceful way of life and difficult-to-get visas. Some people say it's actually easier to climb Mount Everest than to get into Bhutan.  If you can't get there, go to the Sahara Desert. It's 9,065,000 square kilometres, so there should be enough space for everybody!

4 Find some ancient tribes?
Go to Papua New Guinea. First Contact holidays will take you on a three-week trip for $8,000. There, you will trek through the rainforest and search out traditional tribespeople. Kelly Woolford, the boss of Papua Adventures, which runs First Contact, says, 'There are places in West Papua which are untouched [by modern travellers]. People are too scared to go there.'

5 Watch sharks safely?
Visit the Jules Undersea Lodge – an underwater hotel in the Florida Keys, USA. You'll have to dive under the water to get there, but you can see all the big  fish from the windows, including sharks. At $250 a night it's not cheap, but it's not every day you can wave at killer sharks from your window.

Vocabulary | adjectives to describe natural places

1 Complete the sentences with the words from the box.

> deep tropical green rocky
> range desert

Experience the green valleys of Wales. Full board and lodging is included in the price.

1 If you want to escape from the city, Savaii is a _____ island with a difference.

2 The Alps are Europe's greatest mountain _____. You can ski there for nine months of the year.

3 Would you like to go _____ sea diving in the Atlantic? Call us on 0089 27151.

4 Galleton Hotel has unbelievable views of Corsica's _____ coastline.

5 Amazon Tours offer fantastic trips into the heart of Colombia's _____ rainforest.

Grammar | articles

2 Add *a/an* (x 4) and *the* (x 4) to the text where necessary.

Man sent himself in wooden box from New York to Dallas because he thought it was cheapest way to fly.

Charles McKinley, 25, missed his family but thought the flight home would be too expensive. Friend told him it would be cheaper to go as cargo. In fact, cost of sending the wooden box was higher than economy class seat.

After a 15-hour journey in which McKinley had no food or water, box was delivered to his parents' home. McKinley surprised everybody by jumping out of the box. The delivery man called police immediately, and McKinley was arrested.

3 Circle the correct answer: *a*, *the*, or – (nothing).

Bill's Geography website
– for the lost and confused! Send in your questions!

Today's Questions and Answers

1 **Q:** Is Northern Ireland part of *a/–/the* UK?
 A: Yes, but *a/–/the* Republic of Ireland is a separate country.

2 **Q:** Is *a/–/the* Russia in Europe or Asia?
 A: It's in both. Parts of *a/–/the* country are in Asia and other parts are in Europe.

3 **Q:** Where and what are *a/–/the* Andes?
 A: It's *a/–/the* mountain range that runs through several countries in South America.

4 **Q:** What is *a/–/the* sunniest place on earth?
 A: *a/–/the* Sahara Desert. The sun shines virtually all day, every day: 97% of the time.

5 **Q:** Can you tell me about *a/–/the* Monaco?
 A: It's *a/–/the* country in Europe. It's small and rich.

6 **Q:** Is *a/–/the* Nile in Africa?
 A: Yes, it's *a/–/the* longest river on that continent.

7 **Q:** Can you tell me something about *a/–/the* Nauru? I think it's a country.
 A: It's *a/–/the* tiny island in the Pacific Ocean, and you're right – it is a country.

8 **Q:** Is it true that no one lives in *a/–/the* Greenland?
 A: No! But it is *a/–/the* coldest island in the world. 85% of Greenland is covered in ice.

Pronunciation | interest and surprise

4 **6.3** Read the dialogues. Which words does B stress? <u>Underline</u> them. Listen to check.

A: I just returned from a month in Jamaica.

B: Jamaica! That sounds <u>wonderful</u>!

1 **A:** I'm tired.
 B: Really? You slept for ten hours!

2 **A:** I was in hospital for six weeks.
 B: How awful! Are you better now?

3 **A:** I just passed my driving test.
 B: That's great! Congratulations!

4 **A:** It's going to rain tomorrow.
 B: Oh no! I want to go to the beach.

5 **A:** My father was a diplomat.
 B: How interesting! Which countries?

How to ... | show interest and surprise

5 Make echo questions.

I'm from Germany.
Are you?

1   I like travelling.
2   He came here yesterday.
3   It's going to be sunny tomorrow.
4   We'll wait for you at the airport.
5   There's a train at 6.30.
6   They've never been to Paris.
7   She's really friendly.
8   I haven't seen that film yet.

Reading

6   a What do travel agents do?

1   book flights for people ☐
2   tell customers what documents they need ☐
3   help customers get the plane seat that they want ☐
4   find cheap holidays ☐
5   help customers rent cars for their trip ☐
6   tell people which plane to get on ☐

b Read the text. Tick the things from Ex. 6a that are mentioned.

Travel Agents' True Stories

We asked travel agents to write in and tell us about their funniest moments. Here are some of the stories.

I had a client once who called from the airport, saying 'How do I know which plane to get on?' I asked him what he meant and he said, 'I was told my plane was flight 554, but none of these planes have numbers on them.'

A woman phoned me from Detroit. She wanted to know how it was possible that her flight from Detroit left at 8.20a.m. and arrived in Chicago at 8.33a.m. I explained that Chicago was an hour ahead of Detroit, but she didn't understand the idea of time zones. Eventually, I just told her the plane was very fast. She was happy with that.

A man who was travelling to Namibia via London's Heathrow Airport asked if he could rent a car at Heathrow. I noticed that he only had a one-hour stopover in Heathrow Airport, so I asked him why he wanted to rent a car. He said he'd heard that the airport was really big, so he needed a car to drive to his next flight.

c True (T) or false (F)?

1   It takes less than one hour to get from Detroit to Chicago. ☐
2   One man was looking for his flight number on the aeroplanes. ☐
3   A customer wanted to drive from Heathrow Airport to Namibia. ☐
4   A woman didn't want to sit near a window because of her hair. ☐
5   A businessman was going to Colombia for the first time. ☐
6   One customer wanted to smoke on the plane. ☐

d Choose A or B.

1   *Time zone* means
    A   an area where the clocks are set at a particular time.
    B   a place where you go if you are late.
2   *Stopover* means
    A   the place where you finish the journey.
    B   a scheduled stop on a journey, before starting again.
3   An *aisle* seat in a plane is
    A   a seat next to the corridor (not close to the window).
    B   a seat next to the window.
4   *Travel documents* means
    A   a film about a holiday destination.
    B   official papers you need when you travel.
5   *Long haul flight* means
    A   a very large aeroplane.
    B   flight from one continent to another.

One customer was booking a seat on a plane. She asked for an aisle seat so that her hair wouldn't get messed up by being near the window.

A businessman called me about travel documents for Colombia. I told him he needed a passport and visa. He said he didn't need a visa. I checked again and I was definitely right. I called back to explain that he needed it, and he said, 'The last time I was there I didn't need a Visa. They took American Express.'

I booked a customer on a long haul flight from Oslo to Mexico. He asked if it was a non-smoking flight, and I told him it was. He asked if it would be OK to smoke on the plane if he opened the window.

Past Perfect vs Past Simple

1 Choose A, B or C to make the best follow-up to the first sentences.

1 She was amazed when she saw Chartres Cathedral.
   A She had never seen anything so beautiful.
   B She never had seen anything so beautiful.
   C She never saw anything so beautiful.

2 There were crowds of tourists standing around the Mona Lisa.
   A We hadn't expect so many people.
   B We expected so many people.
   C We hadn't expected so many people.

3 The land stretching out in front of us was completely dry.
   A It had rained for months.
   B It wasn't rained for months.
   C It hadn't rained for months.

4 Watching India pass by through the train window, I gradually grew more tired until finally
   A I had fallen asleep.
   B I fell asleep.
   C I lost sleep.

5 Suddenly Janine appeared at my front door.
   A Why she hadn't called first?
   B Why hadn't she called first?
   C Why didn't she called first?

6 The weather was so disappointing during my holiday.
   A I had hoped to spend a few days on the beach, but it was impossible.
   B I hoped to spend a few days on the beach, but it was impossible.
   C I was hoped to spend a few days on the beach, but it was impossible.

7 Poland is one of the most interesting countries I've ever been to.
   A I'd gone there last August.
   B I'd been there last August.
   C I went there last August.

8 The hotel looked great, but they didn't give us a room because
   A we didn't book.
   B we hadn't booked.
   C we not had booked.

Past Perfect and articles

2 Circle the correct word in *italics*, and put the verb in brackets into the correct tense (Past Perfect or Past Simple).

1 She was sad because she found out that she _____ (fail) *a/an/–/the* final law exam.

2 I wanted to become *a/an/–/the* doctor. But in the end I _____ (become) a nurse.

3 I arrived at *a/an/–/the* party at 8.oo but I _____ (not stay) long. What about you?

4 He got hurt during judo. Later they discovered that he _____ (break) *a/an/–/the* his leg.

5 *A/An/–/The* computers _____ (start) to become popular with the public in the 1990s.

6 When they returned, *a/an/–/the* children _____ (already fall) asleep.

7 That afternoon I told the police that I _____ (not recognise) *a/an/–/the* burglar's face.

8 I'm sure we can find *a/an/–/the* good café. There were lots when I _____ (come) here in 2004.

9 It seemed like *a/an/–/the* interesting programme. I _____ (never see) it before.

10 *A/An/–/The* lions tend to sleep during the day. When I _____ (go) to Africa, I saw a few.

Uses of *like*

3 Rewrite the sentences/questions using the words in *italics*. Use *like*.

1 Tell me about Warsaw.
   What's _____?

2 Do they want some milk?
   Would _____?

3 I'm not interested in being famous.
   I wouldn't _____.

4 Tell me about Johnny's appearance when you last saw him.
   What did _____?

5 It tastes the same as meat.
   It _____.

6 Can you describe robots of the future?
   What will _____?

7 I've never been keen on rock music.
   I've never _____.

8 Is Spanish grammar similar to Portuguese grammar?
   Is _____?

9 Luisa and her sister, Daniela, look the same.
   Luisa _____.

10 Mum, how was life in the 1960s?
   Mum, what _____?

Articles and uses of *like*

4 a Some of these sentences need *a/an* or *the*. Add them where necessary.

1 It's small, pretty town in the south of England, famous for cider, a drink made with apples. ☐
2 They're tall and handsome, and oldest one has really good sense of humour. ☐
3 No! I think it's the most disgusting food I've ever eaten! ☐
4 Horses. I wanted to be horse trainer when I was younger. ☐
5 It was brilliant place. Owner was very friendly. ☐
6 My mother, I think. We have similar noses. ☐
7 It's one of biggest buildings in city, and it's made of glass. ☐
8 Yes please. Actually, can I have piece of toast? ☐

b Match the statements in Ex. 4a to the questions below.

a Would you like some bread with your soup?
b What does the Modern Art Gallery look like?
c What's Taunton like?
d Who do you look like in your family?
e What was that restaurant like before it closed down?
f Do you like that Scottish dish, haggis?
g What type of animals do you like?
h What are your cousins like?

Vocabulary

5 a Put the words in the correct box.

| landmark   to the airport   back   lake |
| tropical rainforest   independent travel |
| cruise   sandy beach   castle |
| package holiday   rocky coastline |
| a taxi   camping holiday   directions |
| go on safari   lost   desert   sightseeing tour |

Travel expressions	Places to visit/see	Expressions with *get*

b Cover Ex. 5a. Complete the sentences with one word.

1 I prefer _____ holidays because the hotel and transport are organised for you.
2 I'd like to go on _____ because I love seeing wild animals, especially in Africa.
3 The public transport from the airport isn't good. It'll be easier to get a _____.

4 If you love holidays on the ocean and you have enough money, you should go on a _____.
5 We need to take a map; in Venice it's easy to get _____.
6 The Eiffel Tower is Paris's most famous _____. It dominates the city's skyline.
7 If you want to see the most famous places in the city, go on a _____ tour.
8 We leave for Tunisia on the 30th and get _____ on the 7th.
9 I don't like _____ holidays because I hate staying in tents and living outside!
10 There are some tribes still living in the tropical _____ in Brazil.

6 Use an expression with *get* to replace the words in *italics*. Use the correct verb tense.

1 They decided to *have their wedding* in Florida. _____
2 I really think my English is *improving*. _____
3 We're *returning* before 5.00. _____
4 He's always *had a great relationship with* his mother-in-law. _____
5 I usually *put on my clothes* at about 8.00 in the morning. _____
6 She wanted to go home, but she *couldn't find the way*. _____
7 When will we *arrive at* the airport? _____
8 I was learning the game, but I *lost interest* and stopped. _____
9 Nearly 50 percent of married couples *end their marriage* after ten years or less. _____
10 I'll *buy* you a drink later. _____

How to …

7 Add a word to each line that A says.

1 **A:** Excuse me. Is a Post Office near here?
   B: There's one on your left.
2 **A:** Can you tell the way to the theatre, please?
   B: Yes. Go straight on. It's right in front of you.
3 **A:** What time the museum close?
   B: At 6.30.
4 **A:** How is a ticket to the city centre?
   B: €3.20.
5 **A:** Excuse me. Could you tell me to get to Eve's Restaurant?
   B: Eve's Restaurant? Sorry, I don't know it.
6 **A:** Does this train go the airport?
   B: Yes, it does.
7 **A:** You know how much a hire car costs per day?
   B: It's about £20, not including insurance.
8 **A:** Can recommend a good nightclub?
   B: Yes, Splash Deever is good if you like hip-hop.

Vocabulary | education

1 Choose the correct option.

1 I started playing the trumpet last year, but I haven't *made/done/had* a lot of progress. It still sounds terrible!

2 I'm *making/doing/getting* a Spanish course at the moment.

3 I *made/got/did* law at university.

4 I drank a lot of coffee while I was *passing/failing/revising* for my exams.

5 When I graduated *to/from/at* university, I started looking for a job.

6 I tend to *make/do/take* my research on the Internet.

7 I didn't *make/got/get* good marks in my exams.

8 Did you *take/do/go* notes during the lecture?

9 **A:** Are you coming with us for lunch?
B: No. I'm just *having/going/doing* to my class.

10 I've *got/made/graduated* a degree in English Literature from London University.

2 Complete the dialogues with suitable words.

1 **A:** In this job you need to learn things very quickly.
B: Yes, you are _____ in at the deep end.

2 **A:** I'm not very good at this yet.
B: Keep trying. Practice makes _____.

3 **A:** I can't learn grammar by reading grammar books.
B: No, it's better to _____ by doing.

4 **A:** That's a lovely poem!
B: Yes, I learnt it by _____ when I was at school.

5 **A:** How is your German?
B: Not very good. I keep _____ mistakes.

Grammar | subject and object questions

3 Make subject or object questions using the prompts.

Juliet rang you earlier. Who ...?
Who rang me earlier?

1 Tom took the keys. *Who ...?*

2 Jonathan wanted to talk to you about his article. *What ... about?*

3 Anna-Lisa has moved to the office in Hatfield St. *Which ... to?*

4 The number 42 bus goes to the station. *Which ...?*

5 The history teacher asked me to be here at ten o'clock. *Who ...?*

6 I arrived late. *When ...?*

7 I sold my car to an old friend. *Who ...?*

8 Some of us would like some lunch. *Who ...?*

9 Something has happened to the computer. It's not working. *What ... computer?*

10 A Chinese company is buying the business. *Who ...?*

4 a Write the words in the correct order to make questions.

1 the Cup held World Which 1990 country ?

2 Who presidential Italian election 1997 won the in ?

3 Florence the created Who David in statue of ?

4 city What Pompeii of destroyed the ?

5 the Where Pope live does ?

6 built 1300 Which on islands city is small ?

7 What Italians for lunch usually do eat ?

8 Columbus Where did from sail first Christopher ?

b Match the questions in Ex. 4a with these answers.

a Genova ☐

b A volcano ☐

c In the Vatican ☐

d A dish made with pasta or rice ☐

e Silvio Berlusconi ☐

f Italy ☐

g Michelangelo ☐

h Venice ☐

5 There are mistakes in some of the sentences. Find them and correct them.

1 Who did give Mina my email address?
2 When did you get back from holiday?
3 Who the book belongs to?
4 Who did invent the computer?
5 Who invited Matthew to the party?
6 Which train did they catch?
7 Where lives Marianna?
8 What did happen at the meeting?

Reading

6 These sentences have been taken out of the article below. Read the text and find where they should go.

1 They fail to see them as part of the learning process.
2 Then they restart the computer, and experiment again.
3 People who achieve great success then have more to lose when things go wrong.
4 Learn to talk about your mistakes, at work and at home.

7 What do the words in bold refer to?
Line 2: **it** *making mistakes*

1 Line 9: **them** _____
2 Line 19: **they** _____
3 Line 27: **this** _____
4 Line 30: **this** _____

8 Find words or expressions in the text which mean:

1 make you annoyed _____ (Line 3)
2 fall on the ground _____ _____ (Line 4)
3 saying something with the wrong pronunciation _____ (Line 5)
4 throw and catch three or more balls together _____ (Line 6)
5 the buttons on a computer _____ (Line 16)
6 do something in a way that people don't expect _____ _____ ____ _____ (Line 24/25)
7 do things that could cause problems _____ ____ (Line 29)
8 possibilities for things you can do _____ (Line 31)

Learning from mistakes

Have you ever noticed how children are always making mistakes? They do **it** all the time, and it doesn't seem to bother them. You don't learn to walk without falling over. You don't learn
5 to speak without mispronouncing lots of words. You don't learn to juggle without dropping balls. But if you create an environment where mistakes are not accepted, then people become frightened of **them**. In these kinds of environments people
10 learn to hide their mistakes, and not to celebrate them as a good thing. If you're not making mistakes then you're not learning anything valuable.

Do you remember the first time you touched a
15 computer? You didn't want people to watch you as you started to touch the keys. You worried that if you touched the wrong button, you would delete all the important files. Children aren't like that. **They** experiment with all the buttons, just
20 to see what will happen. And they are learning from every move they make. The fear of failure seems to develop as we go through school. We learn to become afraid of our mistakes, to be afraid of having the wrong answer, or to draw
25 outside the lines.

The fear of success comes later, and we can see **this** often in successful professionals and leaders. So they start to worry, and decide not to take risks.

30 Don't let **this** happen to you. See what opportunities can arise from the mistakes you make, and soon you'll feel happier about yourself.

Vocabulary | adjectives

1 Match the adjectives in the box to the descriptions below.

> patient understanding fierce
> open-minded knowledgeable
> inspiring boring pale

1 Be careful of that dog. He might bite you!
    _____

2 I think she's sick. Her skin looks white. _____

3 His books are wonderful. They give me lots of ideas. _____

4 She can always deal with difficult situations without getting angry. _____

5 He talks too slowly, and doesn't say anything interesting. _____

6 He knows so much about so many things.
    _____

7 You can talk to her about your problems, and she knows how you're feeling. _____

8 He doesn't have fixed ideas about things.

    _____

2 Rewrite the sentences using the words in brackets. You may have to change the tense.

1 She often gets angry. (temper)
2 He talked very loudly to my mother. (shout)
3 She explained things to us well. (clear)
4 He gave extra work to naughty children. (punish/behave)
5 She is friendly and her face always looks happy when she sees you. (smile)
6 Her questions were not easy to answer. (ask/difficult)

Grammar | used to/would

3 Replace the Past Simple with *used to/would* where necessary.

When I was a child ...

1 *I spent my holidays with my grandparents.*
2 *My grandmother cooked delicious meals.*
3 *She kept chickens, goats and horses.*
4 *My cousin and I rode the horses every day.*
5 *My favourite horse was called Racer.*
6 *Racer was faster than all the other horses.*
7 *I didn't understand how dangerous riding could be.*
8 *One day I fell off Racer and broke my arm.*
9 *My mother didn't let me ride him again.*
10 *After that, I sat in the house and watched sadly as the horses played in the field.*

4 a Rewrite these sentences using *used to*.

1 I played volleyball when I was at school. I don't play now.
2 Sylvie doesn't smoke now. Did she smoke before?
3 When I was younger, I didn't like mushrooms. I love them now.
4 I enjoyed cooking a lot before. Now I don't have enough time.
5 She drank milk when she was a child but now she is allergic to it.
6 He didn't play computer games before. Now he is always playing them.
7 I read a lot of books when I was at university. I don't read so many now.
8 You don't study there now, but did you go to the Anglo-American school before?

b In which sentences could you also use *would*?

Listening | childhood

5 **7.1** Cover the tapescript and listen to the description of a young boy called Roger starting school. Then answer the questions.

1 Did Roger like the idea of going to school?
2 When he started school, what did he think was the most important thing to learn?
3 Did he concentrate on learning numbers and letters?
4 By the end, did his teacher think Roger was naughty?

6 Are the following statements true (T) or false (F)?

1 Roger thought he would never grow up. ☐
2 His mother never talked to him about school. ☐
3 Roger was very happy about his first day at school. ☐
4 Roger was put in a class with the big children. ☐
5 He thought the most important thing to do at school was not to move. ☐
6 Roger was punished at school. ☐
7 He thought that if he moved he would get a reward. ☐
8 In his classroom he practised learning numbers and letters. ☐
9 The headteacher asked if Roger was a naughty boy. ☐
10 Miss Bradshaw said that Roger's behaviour was better. ☐

Pronunciation | silent letters

7 **a** Underline the silent letters in the following phrases from the listening passage.

1 ... I thought to myself ...
2 ... my mother would mention ...
3 ... she was talking ...
4 ... the naughty children ...
5 ... less trouble than he used to be ...

b **7.1** Listen again to check. Practise saying the phrases.

c Underline the silent letters in the words in the box. Then write the words in the correct places in the table.

> used to   thought   knew   walk   saw
> should   naughty   knee   talk   bought
> taught   would

silent *gh*	silent *l*	silent *w*	silent *d*	silent *k*

d **7.2** Listen to check.

TAPESCRIPT

I was born on the 4 November 1956. I think I always thought that I would spend my whole life just being a child, and living at home with my parents. Sometimes my mother would mention something called 'school', but she always said that I didn't need to worry. I didn't understand this, as whatever 'school' was, I didn't plan to go there. Then, one morning, she woke me up early and said, 'Today you go to school, Roger.' I was terrified, and thought to myself, 'This is the end of my life.'

That first day at Elementary School I quickly came to understand the most important thing about education – it was all about keeping still. As I entered the hall, a large hand took me away from my mother, and put me in a line with some other small children. And then a loud voice commanded 'KEEP STILL!' I stood very, very still, thinking that if I even moved one small part of my body, I would get some terrible punishment. I checked my body – feet and legs – keeping still, body and arms – keeping still, head and eyes – oh no – what about my eyes? Were they moving?

Inside the classroom, there were the same rules. I was put behind a desk and all I can remember was this tall, thin lady – Miss Bradshaw, our teacher – who kept shouting at us to 'Keep still!' while she was talking. 'How can I write and keep still?' I thought. 'Can I open my book?' After a month the situation was the same, and instead of concentrating on unimportant things like learning numbers and letters, I spent all my time practising very hard the art of keeping still.

I was rewarded, as one day the headteacher came into the classroom. 'Stand up for the Headmistress!' shouted Miss Bradshaw. 'Who are the naughty children?' asked the headteacher. 'What about you, Roger?' I stood very still and tried to look serious. Miss Bradshaw replied, 'No, not any more. Roger is much less trouble than he used to be,' and I smiled a long, warm smile.

Vocabulary | old age

1 Complete the text with the words from the box.

> senior citizens   pensions   elderly
> retire   nursing homes   respected

● Too old to care?

I think the way old people are treated in this country is terrible. When I (1)_____, I'd like to live in my own house by the sea, in a society where old people are (2)_____ because of their age and experience, not robbed in the street. If I am unable to look after myself when I become (3)_____, I hope that someone in my family, or perhaps a close friend, will be able to help me. It's sad that (4)_____ have to go into (5)_____ when their families don't have the time to help look after them. The government doesn't do enough to help old people either. Most people's (6)_____ are very small, they don't have enough money to live off.

Grammar | *could/was able to/managed to* for past ability

2 Complete each sentence using the verbs in brackets and one of the verbs from the box. You may need to change the tenses.

> tell   publish   play   write   read   paint

1 Pablo Picasso _____ from a very young age. He had his first exhibition in La Coruna, Spain, at the age of thirteen. (could)

2 The world's youngest college graduate, American Michael Kearney _____ his doctor 'I have an ear infection' when he was only six months old. (able)

3 Mozart was a very young composer. _____ his first minuet for the piano when he was only five years old. (manage)

4 William James Sidis, who was perhaps one of the most intelligent people ever, _____ Homer, in Greek, when he was four years old. (able)

5 The Swiss psychologist, Jean Piaget, wrote and _____ his first scientific paper at the age of ten. (manage)

6 Yehudi Menuhin _____ the violin so well that he had his first major public performance aged seven. (could)

3 Complete the sentences using the words from the box.

> managed to   able to   could   managed
> were   didn't manage to   couldn't   wasn't
> wasn't able to   able

1 I _____ pass my driving test until I was thirty.

2 Tim wasn't _____ swim at school because of his ear infections.

3 We were sitting near the back of the concert hall but we _____ hear the music beautifully.

4 _____ you able to see the actors without wearing your glasses?

5 I played rugby at school, but I never _____ get into the team.

6 We _____ walk to school as children because it was too far.

7 Abigail was _____ to read music when she was only four years old.

8 Boris _____ able to join the choir because his voice was too quiet.

9 He _____ to learn the music off by heart.

10 Susan _____ sing because she had a sore throat.

Reading

4 Read the text and choose a suitable title for the article.

> 1 **Not old enough**
>
> 2 **Can't wait to retire**
>
> 3 **Not the retiring type**

5 What is the importance of the following numbers from the article?

> 56 years   9.30   70   4 million   40 hours
> 72   1945   94   90s

6 Answer the questions.

1 What three things does the article suggest people can do more of when they stop working?
2 What does Dorothy Beckett's work involve?
3 How old are some of her colleagues?
4 Would Dorothy like to stop work?
5 Did William Spencer always want to be a car salesman?
6 Why didn't he become a lawyer?
7 Why does he believe the company is still happy to pay him?
8 What hours does Gerald Lilley work when he is not travelling?
9 Where does he live?
10 What makes him tired nowadays?
11 What does he enjoy doing to relax?

Retirement – surely it's a golden age when you can escape the daily grind of work and spend your time doing gardening, taking holidays and chatting with friends? Not for everyone. Some people love their work so much that they stay on into their 70s, 80s and 90s.

The factory worker

Dorothy Beckett, 93, has been working in a cake factory in Yorkshire, UK for more than 56 years. She works a 40-hour week, putting cakes in boxes, together with people who are 70 years younger than her. In 1945, aged 36, Dorothy set up the factory with her husband, Fred. Now, the business has a £4m annual turnover. 'I've never wanted to retire,' she says. 'It would be the end of me.'

The car dealer

William Spencer wanted to be a lawyer. But when he discovered that he didn't have the right qualifications, he studied accountancy at night school instead and got a job in a car sales showroom. That was 72 years ago, and he is still there today! 'I'm paid for my experience,' explains William, 91. 'I help the young ones to sell. I advise the staff, introduce customers, arrange special deals, deal with problems, and make sure everyone is happy.'

The banker

'In the past year I've travelled to London, Paris and Milan for work,' says Gerald Lilley, sitting with a poetry book on his knee in his apartment in New York. 'I've been to London three times, to Japan twice and to China, well, lots of times. When I'm not travelling, I like to be in the office every day at about 9.30. And I tend to leave at around 4.00 p.m. Mr Lilley is 94, and is senior advisor at one of the big investment banks. He finds the flights more tiring nowadays, especially after long days in meetings. 'I suppose it's my age,' he says, 'but I have my evenings to relax, have a drink and read German, French and English poetry.'

Vocabulary

1 Answer the clues to complete the crossword.

Across

2 She _____ from university with an Honours degree in Economics.

5 I think I've made a terrible _____.

7 I'm doing an art _____ in the evenings.

8 Unfortunately, you _____ the exam.

Down

1 I'm not very good yet, but I'm making _____.

3 Have you _____ for the history test?

4 We've been doing some _____ into why people eat fast food.

5 Did you get good _____ in your exam?

6 His lectures are so memorable you don't need to take _____.

Subject/object questions

2 There are mistakes in some of the questions. Correct them.

1 Who did go to the meeting?

2 Which room did they go to?

3 What did happen?

4 Where did was Shakespeare born?

5 Who did write *Macbeth*?

6 Which character did you like best?

7 Who did telephone the engineer?

8 What did he say?

9 When did you see her?

10 Who did eat the cake?

Vocabulary

3 Complete the sentences using words from the box.

> practice   heart   brought   learner   curve   thrown   perfect   strict   picked   steep   fast   deep

1 I learn things quickly. I'm a _____ _____.

2 We couldn't play in her lessons. She was a very _____ teacher.

3 Just keep trying and you'll get better. _____ makes _____.

4 I have learnt so much in the first week. It's a _____ learning _____.

5 I can sing all the Beatles' songs from memory. I learnt them by _____.

6 I didn't have Spanish lessons. I just _____ it up when I was there on holiday.

7 We didn't have any training. We were just _____ in at the _____ end.

8 I was _____ up to respect older people.

Adjectives in descriptions/ professional qualities

4 Replace the words in brackets with a suitable word to complete the sentences.

1 She looked tired, and her face was p_____ (her skin was white).

2 She's a tall, s_____ (thin) lady with long, dark hair.

3 Be careful. That lamp is very f_____ (easily broken).

4 She was such a m_____ (gentle) old lady.

5 I don't like that dog. It can be very f_____ (aggressive).

6 Have you seen their new house? It's g_____ (huge).

7 My parents were o_____ – m_____ (they weren't closed in their way of thinking).

8 My uncle was very k_____ (he knew a lot) about the war.

9 He l_____ his t_____ (gets angry) if things go badly at work.

10 I explained the problems and he was very u_____ (he knew how I felt).

used to/*would*/Past Simple

5 Tick the correct options. There may be more than one correct option.

1 When I was a boy I _____ a bicycle.
   A use to ride
   B used to ride
   C would rode

2 As a girl she _____
   A always loving paint.
   B always would love painting.
   C would always love painting.

3 We _____ in a huge house in the countryside.
   A would live
   B used to live
   C lived

4 My grandfather _____ me how to cook.
   A would show
   B showed
   C use to show

5 I didn't _____ listening to opera music.
   A use to enjoy
   B enjoyed
   C would enjoy

6 He once _____ me he would never leave.
   A used to promise
   B would promise
   C promised

7 As children we _____ very naughty.
   A were
   B used to being
   C would be

8 Yesterday, I _____ to the cinema.
   A used to go
   B went
   C would go

6 Use the words in the box to complete the sentences.

> pension   nursing home   elderly
> senior citizen   respect   retire

1 I want to work all my life. I would never _____ .

2 I earn quite a lot of money, so I try to save some for my _____ .

3 It's great. As a _____ I get free public transport.

4 She was very old and had spent the last few years in a _____ .

5 There isn't enough _____ for _____ people in this country.

Ability: past and present

7 Choose the correct answer.

1 Ivan *could/was able to/managed* to get us some tickets for the show.

2 We *managed not to/couldn't/didn't able to* see properly because we were in the back row.

3 Were you *able to/could/manage to* read my handwriting?

4 I didn't *could/able to/manage to* send him a message in time.

5 Problems meant that they *weren't able/couldn't/didn't manage* finish the job.

6 Did you *manage to/could/able to* get her autograph?

7 I *didn't manage/wasn't able to/couldn't to* swim until I was 22.

8 She *couldn't/didn't manage/wasn't able* understand my accent.

9 I *was able/could/managed* speak three languages before I was six years old.

10 We *weren't able to/didn't could/didn't manage* contact you immediately.

Vocabulary | idioms about learning

8 Use words to complete these idioms about learning.

1 I didn't _____ a clue what to get her for her birthday.

2 The translation was very difficult so Ella _____ me a hand.

3 She asked me for the price so I made a _____ guess.

4 I picked _____ a lot about company law when I worked in a law firm.

5 She always gives him top marks for his work because he is the _____ pet.

6 She is always in her study reading books. She is a real _____ .

7 I'll need to _____ up on my Russian if I am going to work there.

8 He knew the building inside _____ .

9 Irregular verbs are difficult. You just have to _____ them by heart.

10 She passed the exam with flying _____ .

Vocabulary | phrases with *change*

1 Use phrases with *change* to complete the sentences.

1 He used to be a lawyer, but then he _____ and became a professional artist instead.

2 It was obvious that I had said the wrong thing, so I quickly _____ the _____.

3 I'm so pleased that you had a _____ of _____ and decided to come after all.

4 I was planning to go out with everyone from work tonight, but then I _____ my _____.

5 Let's have a curry tonight. It would _____ a _____.

6 I've been working with this company for fifteen years. I think it's _____ for a _____.

Reading and vocabulary | the law

2 Read the article, then complete it with words from the box.

> forbidden   arrested   illegal   fine   offence

Crazy laws

It seems that the Greek philosopher, Aristotle, was right when he said, 'Even when laws have been written down, they ought not always to remain unaltered.' Laws in some parts of the world haven't changed for centuries, and some of them were strange right from the start!

Did you know, for example, that London taxis (officially called Hackney carriages) are still legally required to carry hay and oats for their horses to eat? And in England, it is (1) _____ to stand within 100 yards (91 metres) of the Queen, without wearing socks? It is also illegal for a Member of Parliament to enter the Houses of Parliament, where these crazy laws are made and discussed, wearing a full suit of armour.

If you live in Scotland, however, it's important to know that if someone knocks at the door of your house, and needs to use your toilet, you are legally required to let him in. But if you are Scottish you should stay away from the city of York, in the north of England. There, it is perfectly legal to shoot a Scotsman with a bow and arrow, unless it is a Sunday!

But strange laws don't just exist in the UK. In France, you cannot call your pig Napoleon, and in Italy, a man can be (2) _____ for wearing a skirt. That's not all. In Alaska, USA, while it's legal to shoot bears, waking a sleeping bear to take its photo is prohibited. Still in Alaska, it is considered an (3) _____ to push a live moose out of an aeroplane.

Lots of the craziest laws seem to involve animals. In Hollywood, it is illegal to take more than 2,000 sheep down Hollywood Boulevard at any one time. And in Florida, if an elephant is left tied to a parking meter, the parking fine must be paid, just as it would for a vehicle.

Lastly, children are (4) _____ from going to school with their breath smelling of wild onions in West Virginia. And in Arkansas, teachers who have a certain haircut (a bob) will not be given a pay-rise. In Florida, a woman can be fined for falling asleep under the hair-dryer and unmarried women must not parachute on a Sunday. If they do, they might be arrested, receive a (5) _____ or be put in jail.

3 Answer the questions about the article.

1 What is a Hackney Carriage?

2 In what situation would you have to let a stranger into your house in Scotland?

3 What can happen to men who wear skirts in Italy?

4 Is it all right to take photos of sleeping bears in Alaska?

5 What might happen if you leave an elephant tied to a parking meter in Florida?

6 If you want to earn more money as a teacher in Arkansas, what should you be careful not to do?

4 Look at the pictures and match them to the laws in the article.

Grammar | second conditional

5 Match the sentence halves to make first or second conditional sentences.

1 If we have children
2 We'll see them more
3 If Simon didn't spend all his money
4 If they go on holiday more often
5 He won't watch so much TV
6 What would you say
7 If you won £100 tomorrow
8 We'll spend more time outside

a they will feel more relaxed.
b what would you spend it on?
c when we move to a hot country.
d we'll need a bigger house.
e he could afford to buy a new car.
f if they move to this city.
g if he asked you to marry him?
h if he starts going out in the evenings.

6 Write questions in the second conditional by using the verbs in the box and *would* where necessary.

> can throw try tell find fine drive
> give pick play think smoke hear

1 If you _____ some money in the street, _____ you _____ it up?
2 If a shop assistant _____ you some extra change, _____ you _____ her?
3 _____ you _____ in a public place, if you _____ be arrested?
4 _____ people _____ rubbish in the street if they were _____?
5 If you _____ it was safe, _____ you _____ over the speed limit?
6 _____ you call the police if your neighbour _____ loud music at 2a.m.?
7 If you _____ a couple having an argument in the street, _____ you _____ to stop them?

7 **a** **8.1** Cover the tapescript. Choose the correct options.

1 I *'ll/would* call you tomorrow if I hear from them.
2 If you *want/wanted* a faster car, I'd recommend this one.
3 If there were more police, there *won't/wouldn't* be so much crime.
4 If you *did/didn't* want him to call, you shouldn't have given him your number.
5 If she *stops/stopped* smoking, she'll probably put on weight.
6 Where would you go if you *have/had* a free weekend?
7 If I had some more money, I *will/would* buy that coat.
8 Would it be a problem, if I *will ask/asked* you for some help?
9 The house *will/would* be much cleaner if you helped.
10 We *wouldn't/won't* be here for long, if Eve gets her new job.

b **8.1** Listen to the recording and check your answers. Practise saying the sentences.

> **TAPESCRIPT**
>
> 1 I'll call you tomorrow if I hear from them.
> 2 If you wanted a faster car, I'd recommend this one.
> 3 If there were more police, there wouldn't be so much crime.
> 4 If you didn't want him to call, you shouldn't have given him your number.
> 5 If she stops smoking, she'll probably put on weight.
> 6 Where would you go if you had a free weekend?
> 7 If I had some more money, I would buy that coat.
> 8 Would it be a problem, if I asked you for some help?
> 9 The house would be much cleaner if you would help.
> 10 We won't be here for long, if Eve gets her new job.

Vocabulary | global issues

1 Put the letters in the correct order to make words to complete the sentences.

1 He's always on holiday. He has a wonderful _____ . (sieleftly)

2 The problem in this area is that _____ is getting worse. (ercim)

3 She is researching a _____ for heart disease. (ruec)

4 The _____ in many _____ countries are made worse by _____. (blrspoem/ pongedeliv/raw)

5 If we don't send some food quickly, people will suffer _____. (tirastavon)

6 I recycle newspapers and bottles to help the _____. (meronentinv)

7 _____ has become an important issue since the terrorist attacks. (cyetisur)

8 The _____ of living in _____ countries is very good nowadays. (dtarsadn/ peledodev)

9 There is a factory not far away, which creates a lot of _____. (loitlupon)

10 He is very ill in hospital with a rare _____. (sasiede)

Grammar | adverbs

2 There are mistakes in six of the sentences. Find the mistakes and correct them.

1 I couldn't understand her because she was talking too quick.

2 Be carefully when you turn the light on! The switch is broken.

3 Basically, we need you to start the job as soon as possible.

4 I don't want definitely to be late.

5 We possibly will see her at the theatre.

6 Unfortunately, we couldn't contact Martin.

7 Hopeful she'll call us tomorrow.

8 I completely understand that the situation is difficult.

9 I couldn't see the film clear because I didn't have my glasses.

10 The baby was crying loudly because it was hungry.

3 Complete the sentences with suitable adverbs from the box.

> basically   clearly   personally   really   loudly
> probably   beautifully   unfortunately   completely

1 The music was playing so _____ that I couldn't hear the doorbell.

2 I was sad because _____ we missed the beginning of the film.

3 The manager said that we had to pay, but _____ I don't see why we should.

4 Stan will _____ arrive just as we are ready to leave.

5 I was so _____ exhausted after the journey that I went straight to bed.

6 Could you pass me my glasses? I can't see very _____.

7 I _____ love her new album. She sings _____.

8 The story is complicated, but _____ the thieves get caught as they leave the country.

How to ... | talk about change

4 Complete the news report using words from the box.

> unfortunately   got   more   worse
> surprisingly   still   deteriorated   changes

New reports from the island of Timari indicate that the situation there has (1)_____ overnight. Rebels are (2)_____ surrounding the government buildings and the fighting on the streets has (3)_____ (4)_____. Not (5)_____, shops and businesses have been affected, and people living in the area are becoming (6)_____ frightened. (7)_____, we are not able to bring you a live report, but we will be updating you through the day as the situation (8) _____.

Listening

5 [8.2] Cover the tapescript. Listen to the interview with Paul, a young man who did some voluntary work in Uganda. Answer the questions.

1 Where did Paul go?
2 What was his job?
3 Did he enjoy his time there?

6 [8.2] Listen again. Number the topics in the order that Paul talks about them.

a the problems with the job ☐
b living in England ☐1
c exactly where he was working ☐
d recommending the experience ☐
e making friends ☐
f missing his home ☐
g going home ☐

7 Find words in the text which mean:

1 someone who works without being paid a wage _____

2 areas of Australia and Africa that are in a wild state _____

3 missing home _____

4 give _____

5 someone who performs religious duties _____

6 land along the side of a river or lake _____

7 something that a country/organisation/person has which they can use _____

8 special skills or knowledge that you learn by experience or training _____

TAPESCRIPT

Interviewer: Paul, you were a volunteer in Uganda. Tell me, why did the time you spent there make such a difference to your life?

Paul: I had lived a very quiet life in England. I had never left the country, never been on a plane even. And suddenly there I was on a plane, landing at Entebbe Airport in 40 degrees. I was met by an old priest, and then taken into the bush. It was quite an amazing change – not like anything I had ever experienced in England.

In fact, at the beginning I was very homesick and I just wanted to go back to England, to my friends and family and the life I knew so well. But very quickly I became completely absorbed by what I was doing and by what I was able to offer. People had so little there, and I was able to contribute something. It completely changed my life.

Interviewer: What was life like for you at the time? What were conditions like in Uganda?

Paul: Well, of course, people didn't have much money, but their lives were rich in other ways – family life was very important. But living in the bush was difficult; we were fifteen miles from the nearest post box and fifteen miles from the nearest road. The village was right on the banks of the Nile.

I worked as a doctor seeing about 60 people a day in a small village. Obviously the main problem was that there were almost no resources. That made the work very difficult. But there were positive things too. I made some very close friends during my time in Uganda. And I can certainly say that the journey home, leaving behind the beautiful landscapes and the people I had met, was much more difficult than the journey there.

Interviewer: Would you recommend volunteering to people listening?

Paul: Absolutely. Volunteering is about lending your expertise, whether it is building houses, or understanding people. Most people have something to offer. The experience is an amazing one. It will open your eyes to so many new things and, good or bad, it is hard to see how anyone could possibly regret it.

Vocabulary | life decisions

1 Complete the sentences with verbs from the box. Put them in the correct tense.

> buy go start retire have give up
> leave decide

1 He _____ to study electronics at college.
2 I _____ to university in Boston, and I loved it.
3 I _____ home when I was 18 years old.
4 We are saving so that we can _____ a house together.
5 She is leaving work to _____ a baby.
6 I used to go to the gym every day, but I have _____.
7 I don't think I'll _____ until I'm over 70.
8 He is nearly 40, so if he wants to _____ a family, he needs to think about it now.

Grammar | third conditional

2 Choose the correct options.

1 I _____ bought it if I'd known it would be so difficult to use.
   A would have B wouldn't have C wouldn't
2 We wouldn't have told him if we _____ how he would react.
   A had known B knew C had knew
3 If the tickets had been cheaper, there _____ more people at the show.
   A would been B would have
   C would have been
4 They _____ the booking if they'd thought there would be so many people.
   A wouldn't cancelled B wouldn't have cancelled C haven't cancelled
5 He would have contacted us by now if the car _____.
   A had arrived B has arrived C had arrive
6 They would have told us if the flight _____ delayed.
   A has B had be C had been
7 I would have told you not to come if I _____ that the bank would be closed.
   A realised B had realised C have realised
8 The traffic was so bad it _____ quicker if we had walked.
   A was B has been C would have been

3 Write sentences using the third conditional and the prompts.

1 If there … traffic, she … the plane.

2 If the suit … reduced, the man … able to buy it.

3 If there … water on the floor, the waiter … slipped.

4 They … so wet if they … umbrellas.

5 If they … it would be so busy, they … a table.

6 If he … she had a boyfriend already, he … out to dinner.

Listening

4 **8.3** Cover the tapescript. Listen to Rachel and Justin talking about decisions they have made and make notes in the table.

	What was the decision about?	What was the situation before?	What was the situation afterwards?	Why did they make the decision?	Are they happy with the decision they made?
Rachel					
Justin					

5 Write Rachel or Justin for each statement.

1 _____ had always wanted to help people.
2 _____ wanted to be promoted.
3 _____ was unhappy at university.
4 _____ tries to finish work on time.
5 _____ had studied very hard at school.
6 _____ was often away from home.

8.3 Listen again to check your answers.

6 Are the statements true (T) or false (F)?

1 Rachel found it easy to decide what to do at university. ☐
2 She had always wanted to be a psychologist. ☐
3 Rachel was happy when she got a place at Medical School. ☐
4 She enjoyed her university lectures. ☐
5 Justin was a single man who enjoyed his freedom. ☐
6 When he met Shan the things that were important to him changed. ☐
7 Justin usually works late. ☐
8 He leaves his children with a babysitter so that he can go out in the evenings. ☐

TAPESCRIPT

Rachel:

I think for me the most difficult decision I ever had to make was what to study at university. I started university studying medicine. I'd always wanted to be a doctor and to be able to help people. I'd studied very hard at school in order to pass the exams and get into Medical School. And I was delighted when I managed to. Then, surprisingly, when I started the course, I suddenly found that I wasn't happy with the decision. I didn't enjoy the lectures, and I found working in a hospital environment extremely difficult. I realised that I didn't want to spend the rest of my life doing this job after all. It was a very difficult decision at the time, but I left the university, and I ended up studying psychology instead. I don't regret the decision though. Not at all.

Justin:

I suppose deciding to buy a house and start a family was a big decision. Up until last year my work was the most important thing for me. I worked hard to try and get promoted, and I travelled a lot for business. In my free time, I went out with friends and generally had a lot of freedom. Then I met Shan, and we decided to live together, and my priorities started to change. We got married and started thinking about children. Now I try not to work late, and I've told my boss that I don't want to travel so much. I tend to spend my evenings at home babysitting, but I am happy with the decision. I think it is great to be able to spend time with your children when they are young.

Expressions with *change*

1 **a** Make expressions with *change* using the prompts in the box.

> the subject   my clothes   makes a
> my career   the password   time for a
> her hairstyle   of heart

b Use the expressions in Ex. 1a to complete the sentences. You may need to change the tense.

1 I have been thinking about my job and I think it's time to _____ .
2 I didn't recognise her at first because she's _____ .
3 I asked you how much money you spent. Don't _____ .
4 I couldn't get into the computer programme, because you have _____ .
5 He arrived on time! That _____ .
6 She was going to get married, but she had a _____ .
7 I'll be there in a minute. I just need to _____ .
8 We've been eating pasta all week. It's _____ .

First and second conditionals

2 Choose the correct option.
1 If we *wait/will wait/would wait* here, we'll see them when they arrive.
2 If I were you, I *won't/wouldn't/wasn't* go there.
3 If I *go/went/would go* to university again, I would study sociology.
4 We'll stay in a beautiful hotel if we *go/went/would go* to Prague.
5 If you *gave/give/would give* him some money, he'd stop asking you.
6 She*'ll call/would call/called* us when she gets the message.
7 They wouldn't come unless they *want/wanted/would want* to buy something.
8 She'd be so happy if she *won/win/would win* the race.
9 I *will/wouldn't/won't* know how to contact her unless she gets in touch.
10 You'll fail your exams if you *wouldn't start/didn't start/don't start* revising.

Cause and result

3 Use the words in the box to complete the sentences.

> lead   mean   Therefore   caused   result
> so   because   means

1 Increased numbers of tourists _____ that the sights are busier.
2 More people are using public transport. As a _____ , it's more crowded.
3 Private companies are used to clean hospitals now. This has _____ to dirtier hospitals.
4 More young people are employed, which _____ that it's more difficult for older people to get jobs.
5 Most heart problems are _____ by unhealthy eating habits.
6 Women often give up smoking when they are pregnant _____ of its bad effects.
7 China is a growing economy _____ more and more foreign businesses are moving there.
8 The government gives farmers money to produce crops. _____ , they produce as many as possible.

Global issues

4 Correct the mistakes in the sentences.
1 Starving is a terrible problem in some develop countries.
2 Luckily, they have found cure for this awful diseases.
3 I think my standard living is improved since I come to this country.
4 I don't like the city because there is too much polluted.
5 I think countries should stop to have war. They need to make some peace.
6 Lifestyle of the rich and famous must be very difficult.
7 There is much crimes in this part of the city.
8 We must find a solutions to the problem.
9 Now we can contact people in other countries very easy with the Internet.
10 People all over the world has mobile phones.

How to …

5 **a** Re-order the letters to make words to complete the sentences.

1 Luckily, the _____ (tisuintao) has improved recently. ☐
2 It has got much _____ (tebert). ☐
3 The levels of sales are _____ (tilsl) the _____ (mase). ☐
4 I'm afraid the situation has _____ (etarditeroed). ☐
5 Interestingly, robberies have become much _____ (sels) common. ☐
6 Not _____ (gisiulrspryn), the situation hasn't _____ (denghac) for months. ☐

b Tick the sentences which refer to a change. Put a cross next to the sentences which refer to no change.

Adverbs

6 Choose the correct option.

1 She _____ packed her bags and left.
   A quickly
   B interestingly
   C completely
2 They _____ didn't want us to know about the money.
   A quickly
   B obviously
   C thoughtfully
3 She said the train arrived at two p.m., but _____ it doesn't get here until three p.m.
   A hopefully
   B definitely
   C actually
4 _____, I won't be sorry to see him go.
   A Personally
   B Definitely
   C Really
5 He was always taking days off, so _____ he lost his job.
   A actually
   B definitely
   C not surprisingly
6 The meeting was very long, but _____ they got what they wanted.
   A completely
   B basically
   C personally
7 She's gone to live in Thailand for a year. _____, she'll enjoy it.
   A Surprisingly
   B Personally
   C Hopefully

Third conditional

7 Write third conditional sentences to describe how the situation could have been different. Use the prompts in italics to start the new sentences.

1 I bought a new car. I didn't have enough money to go on holiday.
   If I _____
2 The manager was so difficult to work for we left the company.
   If the manager _____
3 The builders took long lunch breaks. The job wasn't finished on time.
   The job _____
4 It was a sunny day. We sat in the garden eating ice creams.
   We _____
5 She fell and broke her leg. She didn't become a professional dancer.
   If she _____
6 The train was delayed. He arrived late for work.
   He _____
7 I didn't read the contract carefully. I signed it.
   I wouldn't _____
8 When Picasso lived by the sea, he painted such beautiful landscapes.
   Picasso might not _____
9 She lived by herself. She felt lonely.
   She _____
10 John Lennon was a famous rock star. His son became a well-known musician.
   If _____

Vocabulary

8 Add a prefix and/or a suffix to the words in brackets to complete the sentences.

1 I can't trust him any more. He has been so _____. (honest)
2 This fish is _____. It's almost raw. (cook)
3 The _____ is responsible for education. (govern)
4 He went to a clinic for some private _____. (treat)
5 Have you found some cheap _____? (accommodate)
6 He doesn't understand the _____ of saving money. (important)
7 A high level of _____ causes problems for the economy. (employ)
8 The United States of America declared its _____ on 4 July 1776. (independent)
9 There was a powerful student _____ in the 1970s. (move)
10 I don't think it will make any _____. (different)

Vocabulary | work

1 Do the word puzzle by completing the sentences below.

1 He has studied at university so he has the right q_____ for the job.

2 There are a lot of ch_____ when you start a new job.

3 She has worked as a doctor for twenty years so she is very e_____.

4 We are celebrating because Magda has been p_____!

5 The pay is not very good, but we get lots of p_____, like long holidays.

6 It is very tiring because I have to work such l_____ h_____.

7 I need some extra money so I've asked to work o_____.

8 If I get the promotion, I should get a p___ r_____.

9 They will offer me the job if I have got good r_____.

10 Teaching children is hard work, but watching them learn is very r_____.

Grammar | make, let, allow

2 Rewrite the sentences using the verbs in brackets and keeping the same meaning.

1 Our boss doesn't allow us to smoke in the office. (let)

2 Employees can wear jeans to work. (allow)

3 We have to work very hard because of the new manager. (make)

4 Most children are not permitted to watch TV after 10p.m. (allow)

5 The teacher said that we could use our dictionaries. (let)

6 Ruby tells her son to make his bed. (make)

7 Children are not permitted in the club. (allow)

8 The restaurant owner said that my dog couldn't go in the restaurant. (let)

3 Read and complete the email with the verbs from the box.

> allowed   let   make   allowed to
> makes   doesn't let

Hi Michele,
We're having great fun in London, except for the problems with our host family. The lady we are staying with is very strict and she 1)_____ us come home by 10p.m. every evening, so we can't go out with the other students, which is a shame. We aren't 2)_____ to bring friends home either, and she 3)_____ us cook. We have to eat her cooking all the time, and it's terrible! The school is really good though, and we like our teachers. They 4)_____ us study hard, but we're 5)_____ choose which books we use, and they 6)____ _ us talk in Spanish if we need to. Hope you're having a good time on the beach!
Lots of love
Marianna

How to... | present ideas to a group

4 Put the phrases in the correct places to complete the short talk.

> Thank you   Secondly, I'll talk about
> Are there any questions
> The most important thing for us is
> Good afternoon   Our main idea
> I'd like to tell you   In conclusion
> Firstly, I'm going to talk about

1)_____.
2)_____ about Stressbusters. When you are stressed at work what you really need is one of our massages. We offer chair massage and other therapies to help reduce stress at work. 3)_____ why you need Stressbusters. When you sit in front of a computer all day, you do not get enough exercise. If you get angry, the stress goes into your neck and shoulders. This can mean that you don't work well. 4)_____ how a Stressbusters chair massage can help. This chair massage only takes ten minutes, you can stay in your office, it is cheap, and you don't need to take your clothes off. 5)_____ is that a regular massage in the office can help to reduce stress so that you work better, and have a better life. 6)_____ that you don't let stress get worse. 7)_____, our massage stops stress before it becomes a problem. You should try it. 8)_____ for listening. 9)_____?

Listening

5 [9.1] Cover the tapescript. Listen to the recording, then choose the correct answer.
Which questions does the interviewer discuss?

a Should politicians wear suits?

b Is it a good idea for workers to wear casual clothes at work?

c Does wearing a suit at work help you get promoted?

6 [9.1] Listen again. Choose the correct options.

1 Simon Hobbs is *an employee/an employer/a psychologist*.

2 Phone2you employees wear *suits/what they want* to the office.

3 Some psychologists think that wearing casual clothes will mean that workers are *more/less* polite, and will come to work *earlier/later*.

4 Phone2you started to let employees wear their own clothes to work *a few years ago/last year*, and they found that sales *decreased/increased*.

5 Simon believes that wearing casual clothes at work means that workers are more *stressed/relaxed*, they socialise *more/less*, and they leave work *earlier/later*.

6 He says he thinks it makes relationships between workers and their bosses *better/worse*.

7 Simon says some of his clients *do/don't* expect employees to wear suits.

8 He *always/occasionally/never* wears a suit to meetings.

9 He believes that workers should *do what the boss decides/decide for themselves*.

10 He says that nowadays important American and European *sportsmen/politicians and businessmen* wear *casual/formal* clothes.

TAPESCRIPT

Interviewer: Today we're going to talk about casual Fridays. Many businesses nowadays, including some of the big city banks, let their workers wear their own casual clothes to work on a Friday. So, are casual Fridays a good idea? Or are employees who come to work in suits actually more productive than those who come in jeans? Here to talk to us today is Simon Hobbs, who is the managing director of phone2you, a mobile phone company which won the Best Employer of the Year award. Simon, what do you think? How does what you wear affect people at work?

Simon: Well, I think one of the most important decisions we made as a company was to allow employees to wear their own clothes to the office. There are a lot of people who think that if you don't wear a suit at work, you'll be less productive, and that you won't work as hard. Some psychologists say that if your clothes are relaxed, then your manners will be relaxed, and so will your productivity. They think that people won't respect their bosses, and that they'll come to work late.

But we found the opposite. It's true that the way you look affects the way you think, feel and act, but we think that if people are wearing their own clothes, then they're more relaxed, less stressed, and that they'll feel more involved in their work.

Interviewer: I'm sure that's true. So when did your company change its policy on this?

Simon: Quite a few years ago. We started with casual Fridays, and we found that the atmosphere in the office really changed on those days, and sales actually increased. So last year we introduced the idea for every day. I think it helps improve communications between workers and their bosses, and between the workers themselves. You see more young workers laughing and joking, and they actually tend to stay at work later and go out socially afterwards too.

Interviewer: Do some of your customers still expect to see your staff in uniforms or in suits?

Simon: Yes, I think they do. And I do wear a suit sometimes. It's important for people to wear what they feel comfortable in. So if I go to a big business meeting, with important clients, I might wear a suit then. I mean, powerful decision-makers in America and Europe, and in most of the world – they all still dress very conservatively, so there is still a place for that, but I think it's nice to give your employees a choice, and let them decide, rather than make them do something that they are not happy with.

Vocabulary | -ing/-ed adjectives

1 Complete the sentences with the words from the box.

> depressing excited frightening
> confusing frightened bored tiring
> exhausted annoyed relaxing

1 I don't watch horror films. I find them too _____.

2 I'm really _____ about starting my new job. It's going to be great.

3 It makes me sad. The news about the war is very _____.

4 I was so _____ that I left the cinema before the film had finished.

5 When I am stressed, listening to music makes me feel better. It's very _____.

6 I've been working long hours this week, so I'm _____.

7 I don't understand these instructions. They are too _____!

8 Frances was really _____ when she discovered we had spent all the money.

9 I have to carry lots of heavy boxes so my job is quite _____.

10 She started screaming because she was _____ of spiders.

Grammar | reported speech

2 Complete the sentences with *say, tell* or *ask*. You will need to change the tense.

1 Jesse _____ he would see us later.

2 The receptionist _____ us for our passports.

3 The bus driver _____ me where the station was.

4 I _____ her for her telephone number.

5 We _____ we wanted to stay for a week.

6 I _____ you that I would pay for the dinner.

7 He _____ me for the time.

8 I _____ him it was half past three.

9 I'll _____ my mother for some money.

10 I didn't know what to _____ to her.

11 I _____ him your name.

12 He _____ that he had seen her before.

13 We got lost, so we had to _____ for directions.

14 Although he _____ me when the show starts, I've forgotten what he _____.

3 Read what Josie said last year and complete the reported sentences below. Remember to change the tenses.

> My name is Josie and I come from Brazil. I'm living in London and working in a café. I've been here for three months and I really like it, but I miss my family and friends too. I want to go back home at Christmas, but I don't earn very much money so I can't afford the flight. I phoned my brother yesterday and he is going to visit me next month. Maybe I'll ask him to lend me some money. When I eventually go back to Brazil, I will never forget my experiences here in England. I have made a lot of great friends.

1 She said that her name _____ and she _____ Brazil.

2 She said that she _____ in London and _____ café.

3 She said that she _____ for three months and she _____ it, but she _____ family and friends too.

4 She said that she _____ to go back home at Christmas, but she _____ very much money, so she _____ the flight.

5 She said that she _____ her brother _____, and that he _____ to visit _____ the _____ month.

6 She said that maybe she _____ ask him _____ her some money.

7 She said that when she _____ to Brazil, she _____ never forget her experiences in England.

8 She said that she _____ a lot of great friends.

Reading

4 Read the text and match the paragraphs to the summary sentences.

1 Try not to make your colleagues too angry.

2 Some managers will always get angry with people who have just started work.

3 What makes people angry at work?

4 Some managers think that getting angry will make their staff look up to them.

5 If someone gets angry with you, you should try to stay calm.

6 Managers usually have particular things which always make them angry.

The boss from hell?

Do you get angry at work? Yes? Then it's probably because of your manager. Bad management causes more people to lose their temper at work than any other reason. Almost four out of ten people across Europe said that poor management was the issue that makes them most angry about their jobs. In London, one out of three workers would describe their boss as 'the boss from hell!' Read our top tips to help you deal with an angry boss.

1 Understand why the manager is angry

Some managers use fear as a management technique. They think it will make people respect them, although actually it just makes people want to leave their jobs.

2 Know where the anger is directed

Bosses like to get angry with new staff, to see if they can bully them. If you are new to a job, you need to work out if the anger is personal – because you have done something wrong, or business – this is how your manager treats all the new employees. You need to learn not to take things too personally.

3 Identify the danger signs

Learn what are the particular things that make your boss angry. Does he go crazy when colleagues arrive late for work? Does he hate it when a job is not finished on time?

4 Know where to stop

Sometimes the things you do will make other people angry. Learn to watch their reactions so that you can stop in time. If a colleague asks you to go outside for a fight, then you know you have gone too far!

5 Don't meet anger with anger

Try breathing techniques to help calm you down. If someone is shouting at you, try imagining that you are blowing up a balloon. This allows your breathing to slow down and means you are less likely to get angry.

5 Read the text again and find words or phrases in the text which mean:

1 get angry – _____ your _____, go _____

2 bad management – _____ management

3 cope with – _____ with

4 a management style – a management _____

5 look up to someone – _____ someone

6 frighten someone who is smaller or weaker than you – _____ someone

7 decide after thinking carefully – _____ out

8 become quiet instead of being angry – calm _____

9 the opposite of speed up – _____ down

6 Use the words from Ex. 5 to complete this summary.

The article describes how _____ management is the main reason why people _____ their _____ at work, and it offers advice to help workers _____ with a difficult boss. It explains how some managers use anger as a management _____ in order to make employees _____ them. Some bosses may _____ new staff to see how they react. It is important to _____ out why your boss is angry, so that you can try to avoid it. If this doesn't work, and your boss goes _____, the article suggests that you take deep breaths to help slow _____ your breathing, and this will help you to _____ down.

Grammar | past obligation/permission

1 Complete the sentences with as few words as possible to convey the meaning in brackets.

1 We were _____ to smoke at my school. (it was permitted)

2 In my last job we _____ ask the computer engineer to help if we had problems. (it was permitted)

3 I _____ pay the extra money in the end. (it wasn't necessary)

4 _____ you _____ to go to parties when you were younger? (was it permitted?)

5 They _____ to wait for three hours before they were allowed into the exhibition. (it was necessary)

6 I _____ use my mobile phone because I was in the library. (it was not permitted)

7 Did you _____ wait a long time to get a refund? (was it necessary?)

8 We _____ leave our suitcases at the airport so that they could be checked. (we were obliged)

9 You aren't _____ to wear shoes in here. (it isn't permitted)

10 In my last school, we _____ use the Internet for more than twenty minutes. (it wasn't permitted.

Vocabulary

3 Read and complete these job advertisements with words from the box.

> prioritising give type making
> use persuading speak dealing
> work well organising

Bi-lingual secretary required. Needs to be able to (1) _____ fast, and (2) _____ more than one European language.

Marketing Manager required for busy department. Must be able to (3) _____ under pressure, (4) _____ good presentations, and (5) _____ a range of computer software.

PA needed urgently for Chief Executive of HBBS bank. The ideal candidate will be good at (6) _____ with people and (7) _____ decisions. He/She will be good at (8) _____ meetings and (9) _____ his/her busy workload.

Are you good at (10) _____ people to do things? Then you could join our busy sales team and earn extra money working from home. For more details contact Mike.Dodge@workfornothing.com

2 The words in the box have been taken from the text. Tick the lines that are correct and, where a word is missing, write the correct word at the end of the line.

> had couldn't to allowed have could were ~~to~~

1	Schools are different nowadays. They used to be much worse.	✓
2	When I went to school we weren't allowed/wear our own clothes, we	to
3	had to wear a uniform. And our skirts to be long enough to cover	—
4	our knees. Our teacher would make us kneel down and check	—
5	that our skirts touched the floor. We had wear dark, flat shoes,	—
6	with no heels, and we weren't to wear make-up. This was a boarding	—
7	school, so we stayed at the school for the whole term, but	—
8	we allowed to go into town twice a week. I always went with a friend.	—
9	We go to the shops to buy sweets and drinks, or to the library, but	—
10	we go to the cinema until we were in the final year. I used to love the	—
11	summer holidays, when I could go home, and I didn't to follow rules all day long.	—

Reading

Realise your dream...

Do you dream of getting a new job or starting your own business, but worry about how to achieve your dream?

Most of us have dreams, big or small, whether they are to own our own businesses or simply to be happier. Dreams are good because they give us direction and something to focus on.

(1) _____. But often we are so frightened of making changes that we doubt ourselves and our abilities.

'Making your dreams come true usually means making changes to your life, and that frightens many people,' says Kate Emmerson, a life coach who is based in Johannesburg. 'And these changes don't just affect us. They affect the people around us. (2) _____.'

So how can you help yourself to realise your dreams?

'It's important to realise that achieving your dream will take commitment, and it probably won't be easy. Life is a journey of continuous learning, and there may be problems on the way. (3) _____.'

When we have a dream there are a few easy steps we can take to help us achieve it.

You need to be sure that your dream is realistic. (4) _____. Be specific about your dream and make a contract with yourself. Write it down. Seeing your goal in writing, with a date for completion, will help keep you focused.

Find someone to support you and to help you achieve what you need. Usually people ask someone from their family, but they are not usually the best people to ask. (5) _____ Try asking a friend who knows you well and can understand what you want to do.

List your obstacles – the things that might get in the way of your dream – and work out how you will overcome them. Spend thirty minutes each day doing something towards your dream. Perhaps the most important thing to do is ask yourself each day, 'What is the single thing that I can do that will take me just one step closer to my dream?' (6) _____.

4 Read the article, then choose the best summary sentence. The article:

1 talks about the meanings of dreams.

2 gives advice to people who can't sleep.

3 gives advice about how to achieve your dreams.

4 tells people how to know if they are dreaming.

5 The following sentences are from the article. Use them to complete the gaps 1–6.

a Don't set goals that are impossible to achieve.

b How we react to those problems will depend on how strongly we want to reach our goals.

c Remember to keep it simple, and take it just one step at a time.

d They don't necessarily mean that we are unhappy, but they help to pull us forward to do new things.

e They are happy with you as you are.

f And often the people around us, our friends and family, don't want us to change.

6 **a** Match the words in A to the words in B.

A

1 make your dreams

2 realise

3 take one

4 get in

5 set a

B

a your dreams

b the way

c come true

d goal

e step at a time

b Complete the advice, using one of the expressions in Ex. 6a.

1 It's impossible to achieve everything immediately. You have to _____ .

2 You must be determined to succeed. Don't let anything _____ .

3 When you _____ , be realistic.

4 You have to work hard if you want to _____/_____ .

Vocabulary: jobs

1 Choose the correct option.

1 I *retired/applied/worked* for a job as a police officer, but I didn't get it.

2 He was made redundant from his job, so now he is *unemployed/overtime/retired*.

3 The advantage of my work is that I can work *rewarding/challenges/flexitime*.

4 One of the biggest *challenges/rewarding/pay rise* was learning a new language.

5 She works such *overtime/long hours/all day* that she should get a *promoted/rewarding/pay rise*.

6 He's been doing the job for years so he's very *rewarding/experienced/references*.

7 I'm *applying/experienced/promoted* for a new job, so I need to ask you for a *perks/CV/reference*.

8 JM just got *a job/pay rise/promoted* to senior manager.

9 The pay isn't very good. Are there any *perks/pay rise/references*?

make, let, allow

2 Correct the errors in these sentences, but keep the same verbs.

1 We not allowed to go into the conference hall.

2 She wouldn't let me to see a doctor.

3 They should to make her get a job.

4 Did they make you filling in a form?

5 Am I allow to smoking?

6 The landlord doesn't to let us have parties.

7 Her parents let to her to do anything she wants.

8 He's angry because we won't let he go to the cinema alone.

9 Why don't we allowed to speak during the test?

10 When we play chess together, my father always let that I win.

How to ...: present ideas to a group

3 Put the words in the correct order to make sentence openings.

1 about you to like tell I'd

2 talk I'm about to going , Firstly

3 for important us most thing The is

4 is main idea Our

5 I'll about , talk Secondly

6 up To sum

Vocabulary

4 Choose the correct option.

1 If I am feeling *tired/tiring* at the end of the day, I have a bath and read my book. I find it very *relaxed/relaxing*.

2 He's *frightened/frightening* of dogs.

3 I can't wait to see you again after all this time. I'm so *exciting/excited*!

4 He never says 'please' or 'thank you'. It's really *annoying/annoyed*.

5 I'm not very good with figures. I find them too *confused/confusing*.

6 He's a bit *depressed/depressing* because he can't find a job.

7 I have been working long hours, so I'm *exhausted/exhausting*.

8 I can't stand that soap opera. It is so *bored/boring*.

9 They were *rewarded/rewarding* when they found the camera.

10 The documentary film was very *interesting/interested*.

Reported speech

5 Complete the sentences with *say/tell/ask*. You may need to change the tense. There may be more than one possibility.

1 My boyfriend _____ me to marry him!

2 We _____ her to meet us at the station.

3 The interviewer _____ us if we had enjoyed making the record.

4 Why didn't you _____ me before?

5 We _____ for some free tickets, but the manager _____ 'no'.

6 He _____ he would be here by two o'clock.

7 They _____ us whether we liked living in Edinburgh.

8 I _____ I would do the work as soon as possible.

9 She _____ me how much it cost, so I _____ her.

10 They _____ there's another hotel just round the corner.

Reported speech 2

6 Choose the best option.

1 He _____ my daughter to be quiet.
   A said
   B told
   C asked to

2 She _____ it was the best holiday she had ever been on.
   A told
   B said me
   C said

3 They _____ that I would be late for the meeting.
   A told
   B asked
   C told me

4 'I have been here for too long.'
   She told me that she _____ for too long.
   A had been there
   B had been
   C have been here

5 'Would you like to come to my house for dinner?'
   She asked me _____ for dinner.
   A if I like to go to her house
   B if she wanted to go to my house
   C whether I wanted to go to her house

6 'The car will be ready tomorrow.'
   He said that the car _____.
   A will be ready the next day
   B would be ready the next day
   C had been ready tomorrow

Past obligation/permission

7 Complete the sentences with *could/couldn't, was(n't)/were(n't) allowed, had to, didn't have to.*

1 At school, we _____ play outside in the rain. (It was necessary)

2 My brother _____ show his passport at customs. (It wasn't necessary)

3 As children, we _____ to talk at the dinner table. (It was not permitted)

4 We _____ play football every afternoon. (It was permitted)

5 I _____ to drive my father's car. (It wasn't permitted)

6 Unfortunately, we arrived late so we _____ sit at the back. (It was necessary)

7 The talk wasn't very interesting because we _____ ask questions. (It wasn't permitted)

8 I hope you _____ wait too long. (It wasn't necessary)

Job requirements

8 Complete the sentences with words from the box.

> prioritise   accurately   irregular   figures
> decisions   presentations   pressure
> delegating   range   long   solving

1 As a sales team, we have to give good _____.

2 I'm a taxi driver so I work _____ and _____ hours.

3 I work as a therapist, so I'm quite good at _____ problems.

4 Here in air traffic control, the most important thing is to work very _____.

5 In the office I use a _____ of computer software.

6 I use an accountant because I'm not very good at _____.

7 I try to do everything myself because I am no good at _____.

8 I have too many things to do, so I have to _____ my work.

9 I couldn't be a manager because I can't make _____.

10 I actually have my best ideas when I'm working under _____.

Vocabulary

9 What is the American- or British-English equivalent to the words in italics?

1 I *mailed* her a letter this morning. _____

2 We went home to watch a *film*. _____

3 I need to move out of my *apartment* on Friday. _____

4 Where did you go to *secondary school*? _____

5 Did you watch the *football* match? _____

6 Excuse me. Where is the *restroom*? _____

7 I'll see you in the *shopping centre*. _____

8 We need to stop for *gas*. _____

9 Did you bring your *cell phone*? _____

10 He was driving at 150 k.p.h. along the *highway*. _____

11 You mustn't cycle on the *sidewalk*. _____

12 I'm sorry, but the *lift* is out of order. _____

Vocabulary | verbs connected with memory

1 Select the correct words in italics.

1 We must *remind/remember* to buy some milk. We haven't got any left.

2 Hurry up! You're going to *miss/lose* the train.

3 This house *reminds/remembers* me of the place where I used to live.

4 I keep *forgetting/missing* to pay my phone bill.

5 Can you *remind me to/remind me of* call Robin? I need to speak to him.

6 I've *forgotten/lost* my key. I can't find it anywhere.

7 Do you *remind/remember* the day we met?

8 This programme *reminds me of/reminds me to* a film I saw last week.

9 Living so far away, do you *lose/miss* your family?

10 I've *missed/forgotten* how to play this game.

Grammar | wish/if only

2 Use two or three words to complete the second sentence of each pair so that they mean the same as the first sentence.

1 We haven't got any matches to light the fire.
I wish _____ some matches.

2 I can't afford that skirt.
I wish _____ that skirt.

3 She is very sad that she missed your wedding.
She wishes _____ your wedding.

4 You always make a mess in the kitchen!
I wish _____ make a mess in the kitchen!

5 We were late for the train, so then we missed our flight!
If only _____ late for the train!

6 You live too far away, so we never see each other.
If only _____ closer to me.

7 I can't do this biology homework. It's too difficult.
I _____ better at biology.

8 I love China but I can't speak the language.
I wish _____ Chinese.

9 I ate a disgusting pizza.
I wish _____ that pizza.

10 You're always complaining!
I wish _____ stop complaining!

3 What do these people wish? Write sentences using the phrases from the box.

> not be so short   not buy this car
> have more money   revise   can run faster
> not go skiing

Vocabulary | nature collocations

4 Which collocation in each group is not possible?

1 The wind
   A was blowing all night.
   B was very strong.
   C was bright.

2 We heard
   A them riding their horses.
   B the shouting of horses.
   C the hooves of horses.

3 She walked slowly through the
   A strong wood.
   B dark wood.
   C dense wood.

4 The snow
   A flakes came down.
   B fell all night.
   C dripped fast.

5 From our boat we saw the
   A back of the lake.
   B shore of the lake.
   C frozen lake.

Reading

5 **a** What do you think a 'brain pill' does?

A Destroys bad memories

B Makes you more intelligent

C Improves your memory

D Helps you read another person's mind

Now read the text to find out.

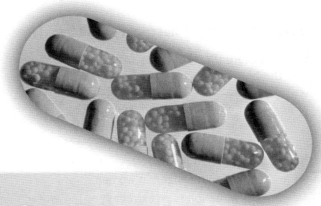

Instant Memory

1 Imagine the scene: you have an important exam tomorrow morning. Your future depends on it. You stay up all night, drinking endless cups of coffee, trying to memorise four years' information in twelve hours. Sounds familiar? But imagine you didn't need to do this. Imagine you could just take a pill and immediately remember everything.

2 A memory pill, or any other pill that wakes up the brain, is a great idea, not only for students, but for lots of other professions. Soldiers, who have to function with just a few hours' sleep, would welcome it. So would pilots on long trips, and shift workers who have to work with heavy machines at night. So too would the 37 million people around the world who suffer from Alzheimer's Disease, an illness that robs people of their memory.

3 But are we close to finding such a pill? A number of pharmaceutical companies are already working on it. They see enormous financial possibilities in a pill that increases the memory, and laboratories have already been testing pills on both animals and humans.

4 But a memory pill raises ethical questions too. History tells us that the pill would be used not only by ill people, but also by people who just wanted to remember everyone's name at parties, or the laziest students. Is this fair on poorer students who couldn't afford the pill? Would businesses start asking their workers to take pills so that they performed better? Would we divide quiz shows into two types: contestants with brain pills and contestants without?

5 Medicine and its processes evolve. Often, the original purpose gets lost. This has happened with plastic surgery (originally for soldiers with injuries to the face; now used by middle-aged actors who want to stay prettier for longer) and it happened with Prozac. It may happen with cloning. The truth is, we don't know how a memory pill would affect society. Fortunately, we probably have a few more years to think about it. Most scientists believe that the drugs need much more testing. Some of these drugs work well with animals, but, as Dr Sue Clarke, one of the scientists working in this area, says, 'It isn't clear that animals use the same kind of memories as humans. A mouse doesn't have to remember a shopping list during the day.'

b Answer the questions.

1 Why would soldiers like a brain pill?

2 Which 37 million people would welcome a brain pill?

3 What are a number of pharmaceutical companies trying to do?

4 What ethical question does the text ask about students using brain pills?

5 What might businesses begin to do, according to the text?

6 How has the use of plastic surgery changed?

7 How long will we have to wait for the brain pills?

8 How does Dr Sue Clarke compare humans' memories and animals' memories?

c Match the headings to the correct paragraph.

a What usually happens with medicine? ☐

b Questions society needs to ask ☐

c The solution for exam students! ☐

d Who needs a 'brain pill' at work? ☐

e Big businesses searching for 'brain pill' ☐

d Complete the summary of the text. Use one word in each gap.

Brain pills would be welcomed by students who were studying for (1)_____. Many professions would also use them: for example, people who (2)_____ in shifts, pilots and soldiers who don't get much (3)_____. But brain pills raise many (4)_____ too, about how society would use them. Many scientists say that the pill needs to be (5)_____ more, before we can use it safely.

Vocabulary | describing great people

1 Complete the sentences with words from the box.

> talented   encouraged   courage
> determined   dedicated   involved

1 Maryam Babangida is _____ to improve education for Nigerian women.
2 Toni Morrison is an extremely _____ writer. She won the Nobel Prize for Literature in 1993.
3 Rigoberta Menchu _____ her life to the poor people of Guatemala.
4 Amelia Earhart had the _____ to fly alone across the Atlantic.
5 Wangari Maathai is _____ in politics in Kenya. She won the Nobel Peace Prize in 2004.
6 J K Rowling's Harry Potter books have _____ many young children (and some adults!) to read.

Grammar | past tenses review

2 Choose the correct verb tense.

1 By the age of twenty, Linda Evangelista *had already been/was already* a model for five years.
2 Fourteen-year-old Kate Moss *walked/was walking* in JFK Airport when a fashion agent first saw her.
3 Naomi Campbell started modelling as a teenager, and then *wrote/had written* a novel in 1995.
4 When Cindy Crawford became a model, she *already started/had already started* a university degree in chemical engineering.
5 Julia Roberts made her first film at twenty. Before that she *was being/had been* a model.

3 Complete the sentences by putting the verb into the Past Continuous or Past Perfect.

1 After we _____ (know) Michelle for a few months, we invited her over for lunch.
2 Paul arrived four hours late. He explained that his car _____ (break down) in Lyon.
3 Oh sorry, _____ (you talk) to me?
4 When they arrived, it was hot because Mrs Blofeld _____ (switch on) the heating.
5 We _____ (wait) for the bus when it started raining.
6 I first began getting these headaches while I _____ (listen) to rock music.
7 Scotland was completely new to Max. He _____ (go) there before.

4 Complete the text by putting the verb in brackets into the Past Simple, Past Continuous or Past Perfect.

FRIDA KAHLO

One day in 1925, Frida Kahlo (1)_____ (travel) by bus through Mexico City when the bus crashed into a tram. 18-year-old Frida was seriously injured. As a young child, she (2)_____ (already suffer) from polio, but this time, lying in bed for months in terrible pain, she discovered art. She (3)_____ (paint) the things around her, her room, the view from the bed, self-portraits. 'My painting carries with it the message of pain,' she said.

Frida also said, 'I suffered two accidents in my life: one when the tram hit me. The other accident is Diego.' Diego was Diego Rivera, the great Mexican painter who eventually became her husband. It was while she (4)_____ (attend) school that Frida first saw him. A few years later, she saw him again when he (5)_____ (work) on a mural in Mexico City. She showed him one of her paintings. By now, Frida (6)_____ (finish) many pictures, and her work was original and striking. Rivera encouraged her to continue.

In 1930 they (7)_____ (go) to the USA, where Rivera was a great success. Frida hated the country, but during this time she began to paint some of her greatest work. It was while they (8)_____ (stay) in the USA that they both had many affairs, even though they (9)_____ (got) married back in Mexico in 1929.

In 1953, Frida had her first solo exhibition in Mexico. On the day of the opening she was ill in hospital. While the guests (10)_____ (wait) for the exhibition to open, a noisy ambulance came rushing through the street. The ambulance doors opened and Frida was carried into the art gallery, where she (11)_____ (talk), drank and laughed with everybody. Finally, she had achieved fame for herself. By the time she died, she (12)_____ (become) a legend, one of Mexico's greatest painters, whose life still inspires women and men all over the world.

How to ... | say numbers

5 Correct the words which do not match the numbers.

1 two and a half percent = 2.5%
2 one billion = 1,000,000
3 the ninety seventies = 1970s
4 the third of April, two thousand and five = 03.04.05
5 twelve thousand and ninety-eight = 1,298
6 three fours = 3/4
7 eighteen dollars and twenty cents = $18.20
8 ninety-nine and nine percent = 99.9%
9 the twentieth century = C20th
10 forty thousand = 40,000
11 nineteen ninety-six = 1969
12 eleven and half = 11 1/2

6 **a** Write these words in numbers.

four thousand, two hundred and ten – 4,210

1 sixteen thousand, three hundred and forty-nine
_____
2 a third
_____
3 fourteen percent
_____
4 the third of December, two thousand and six
_____
5 eighty-eight dollars, seventy-one cents
_____
6 the nineteen seventies
_____

b Write these numbers and dates in words.

£45.20 – forty-five pounds, twenty pence

1 £23,993
_____
2 3/4
_____
3 99.8%
_____
4 1990s
_____
5 30/12/07
_____
6 20th century
_____

c **10.1** Listen to the sentences. <u>Underline</u> the number or date that you hear.

1 A 4,998 B 4,989
2 A £75.99 B £79.99
3 A 60% B 50%
4 A 16/12/03 B 15/11/03
5 A 6½ B 16½
6 A 1990s B 1980s
7 A 21st century B 20th century
8 A 10th January 1969 B 10th July 1969
9 A 1,000 B 1,000,000
10 A $1,845 B $1,345

d **10.2** Now read the numbers and dates you underlined in Ex. 6c. Listen and check.

TAPESCRIPT

10.1

1 There were four thousand, nine hundred and ninety-eight people at the conference.
2 It costs seventy-nine pounds, ninety-nine pence, which is quite cheap really.
3 We are expecting a fifty percent increase in sales.
4 The programme starts on the fifteenth of November, two thousand and three.
5 I've had the car for about six and a half years now.
6 I listen to a lot of music from the nineteen-eighties
7 There have been changes in transport, even since the beginning of the twenty-first century.
8 I was born on the tenth of July, nineteen sixty-nine.
9 A million men came to Washington that day.
10 This washing machine costs one thousand three hundred and forty-five dollars.

TAPESCRIPT

10.2

1 Four thousand, nine hundred and ninety-eight
2 Seventy-nine pounds, ninety-nine pence
3 Fifty percent
4 The fifteenth of November, two thousand and three
5 Six and a half years
6 The nineteen-eighties
7 The twenty-first century
8 The tenth of July, nineteen sixty-nine
9 A million
10 One thousand three hundred and forty-five dollars

Grammar | phrasal verbs

1 Circle the correct word in each sentence.

1 I hope the band turns *in/up*.

2 I'm going *through/in* a difficult time at work.

3 Excuse the interruption. Please carry *over/on* what you were doing.

4 He called *round/off* the wedding.

5 I hope you can come *up/at* with some better ideas than that!

6 She split *up/off* with her husband after two months.

7 I can't put *up/on* with your behaviour any more!

8 Strange things go *in/on* in this town all the time.

9 If I leave now, I'll never come *off/back*.

10 We need to find *up/out* what time the train leaves.

2 Complete the second sentence of each pair so it has the same meaning as the first. Use two or three words including the verbs in brackets.

1 They stopped going out together a year ago. (split)

They _____ a year ago.

2 The party will be cancelled because of the rain. (call)

They _____ the party because of the rain.

3 Miners tolerate terrible working conditions. (put)

Miners _____ terrible working conditions.

4 I asked her what was happening. (go)

I asked her what _____.

5 I will continue studying until I finish the course. (carry)

I _____ studying until I finish the course.

6 You never arrive on time! (turn)

You always _____ late!

7 Your friend isn't returning today. (come)

Your friend _____ today.

8 We discovered some interesting things yesterday. (find)

We _____ some interesting things yesterday.

9 The team is experiencing a difficult time. (go)

The team _____ a difficult time.

10 We've thought of some new solutions. (come)

We've _____ some new solutions.

Writing | formal vs informal

3 **a** Match the formal phrases, 1–11, to the informal phrases, a–k.

1 I will contact you.

2 Thank you very much.

3 The work has been completed.

4 I look forward to hearing from you soon.

5 Further details can be found on our website.

6 I am writing to enquire about …

7 You are very welcome.

8 I look forward to seeing you soon.

9 Kind regards.

10 I am able to attend.

11 I will arrive at 8.30.

a Best wishes.

b You can get more info on the website.

c I can come.

d You're welcome.

e I just wanted to ask about.

f Write back soon!

g I'll be there at 8.30.

h See you soon.

i Thanks a lot.

j I'll get in touch.

k We've finished the work.

b Complete the emails with phrases from Ex. 3a.

Hi Johnny

(1)_____ for inviting me to the party on Saturday. I love parties and I love London! I asked my parents and they agreed, so (2)_____! My train leaves at 6.30, so (3)_____.

(4)_____ to you and Ruby,

Todd

Hi Todd,

(5)_____! It'll be great to see you! The party is going to be organised by PartyPeople24/7. It should be excellent.

(6)_____ about them. I'm out of town till Friday, but (7)_____ on Saturday afternoon, and I'll meet you at the station. (8)_____.

Johnny

Listening

4 **a** Which of these are good ways of remembering vocabulary? Which ones do you use?

1   Review new words regularly (almost every day). ☐

2   Stick notes around your house with new words on them. ☐

3   Test yourself regularly. ☐

4   Use new words in class whenever you can. ☐

5   Draw pictures of words and phrases. ☐

6   Read your notes before you go to bed. ☐

b **10.3** Cover the tapescript. Listen to two language students discussing how to remember things they learn. Number the things in Ex. 4a in the order that they mention them.

c Listen again and select the best answer.

1   What is their relationship?

   A   They are classmates.

   B   He is her teacher.

   C   They are married.

2   What language are they learning?

   A   French.

   B   Japanese.

   C   Italian.

3   Where does the woman write new words?

   A   On little notes and in a notebook.

   B   On the bedroom walls.

   C   On big pieces of paper.

4   Why should you write new words in your own sentences?

   A   Because Japanese people do this.

   B   Because then you will dream of the words.

   C   Because you can remember them better.

5   What does the woman think is the most important thing for learning new words?

   A   Draw pictures of the words.

   B   Revise regularly.

   C   Study them on the train.

6   Who uses the most learning strategies?

   A   The man.

   B   The woman.

   C   They use about the same number of strategies.

TAPESCRIPT

D: Sally, do you, like, have any good ideas for remembering new words and expressions in Italian? I just can't remember all the stuff we learn.

S: Um, I do lots of things, but I don't know if they'd work for you.

D: Like what?

S: Well, I do things like … um … I put, I stick little notes all over my house with new words …

D: Are you serious?

S: Yeah, I put them on the fridge, on the walls of the bedroom. Just little notes with the words written on.

D: Wow.

S: And I do other stuff like when I'm on the train going to work I take my notebook and test myself. Why, do you …

D: I kind of, well, I tried reading my Italian notes before I went to bed and hoping I'd dream in Italian. But it didn't really work.

S: I think it's a good idea to write the words in new sentences that you invent, so you … um …

D: What, you make up the sentences yourself?

S: Yeah, because then it's easier to remember. Like if you write sentences about your family or friends, you can remember them better.

D: That's a good idea. I like that. What else?

S: A friend of mine who's learning Japanese always draws pictures of words and phrases.

D: Really?

S: She's a, kind of, very visual person and she says she remembers things better if there's a picture. But I suppose, I think the key is to review words regularly. Just keep revising.

D: Like, study them every day?

S: I don't know about every day, but if you review them often enough and try and use them in class or when you're writing, eventually they become part of your permanent vocabulary.

D: D'you think so?

S: I think so, yeah.

wish/if only

1 Choose the correct response.

1 I want to be there with you, but I'm too busy.
   A I wish you were here too.
   B I wish you had been here too.
   C If only you are here too.

2 You're very lazy and your room's a mess and you haven't done your homework.
   A I wish you stop criticising me.
   B If only you shut up!
   C I wish you would stop criticising me.

3 Our exam is on Thursday.
   A If only we won't have to do this exam.
   B I wish we didn't have to do this exam.
   C I wish the exam be on Friday.

4 You didn't have to buy those new chairs. I've already ordered a new sofa.
   A If only you had told me earlier.
   B If only you told me earlier.
   C I wish you would tell me earlier.

5 There's no room for all your friends to stay.
   A I wish there is more room.
   B I wish we were having a bigger house.
   C If only we had a bigger house.

6 You have to keep working. All of this must be finished by five o'clock.
   A I wish you gave me a break.
   B I wish I could take a break.
   C If only I could to stop now.

7 You're too young to come in here.
   A I wish I was older.
   B If only I'm older.
   C I wish I can go in.

8 That film was absolutely terrible.
   A I wish we gone somewhere else.
   B If only we saw a different film.
   C I wish we hadn't wasted our money.

wish/if only and past tenses

2 Complete the second sentence of each pair using the verbs in brackets so that they mean the same as the first sentences.

1 It was my first time in Scotland. (go)
   I had _____ Scotland before.

2 I hate smoking but I can't give up! (stop)
   I wish I _____.

3 When I arrived, the room was clean. (clean)
   She _____ before I arrived.

4 I didn't have time for lunch. (work)
   I _____ so hard that I didn't have time for lunch.

5 That lottery ticket was the winner, but you threw it away! (throw away)
   If only you _____ the ticket!

6 I love tennis, but I'm not very good. (be)
   I wish _____ better at tennis.

7 I didn't introduce Clara to Juan. They knew each other already. (meet)
   I didn't introduce them because they _____.

8 I heard gunshots. I hadn't finished my meal. (eat)
   I _____ when I heard gunshots.

3 Choose the correct verb for each sentence. Put the verb into the correct tense.

> not go   watch   take   leave   already buy
> not stay   not see   try   dance   put

1 I wanted to go to Berlin but my wife _____ tickets to Amsterdam.

2 She _____ TV when the phone rang.

3 I _____ to the show last night because I was working late.

4 I didn't see you arrive at the party because I _____ with my eyes closed!

5 When I got home I noticed that I _____ my wallet in the shop.

6 We peeled the potatoes and _____ them in the oven.

7 David didn't shave last month because he _____ to grow a beard.

8 Mary didn't say hello this morning. Later, she told me that she _____ me.

9 Finally, he passed his driving test. He _____ the test eight times.

10 I went to the Marina to find John, but he _____ there. Maybe he was in the Ibis.

Phrasal verbs

4 Put the words in the correct order to make sentences.

1 picnic raining we because off the was called it.

2 tell can going me what is you on?

3 come a have to with up solution you.

4 turns late Jean up always.

5 can weather up climbers put cold with.

6 out find what last happened night I'll.

7 difficult going a they're period through.

8 back are to planning when come you?

9 times several split they've before up.

10 as as running on long possible for carry.

5 Use a phrasal verb to replace the words in *italics*. Use the correct tense.

I don't know what (1) *is happening* at work. The boss has left, but we (2) *haven't discovered* who is going to replace him. We can't (3) *continue* like this, though. We (4) *are having* the worst economic crisis in years, and there's no one in charge! Actually, I hope the old boss (5) *returns*. He's better than nobody.

Mary suddenly (6) *appeared* at my door in tears yesterday. She was so sad. She told me that she (7) *had ended her relationship* with Bob. I'm not sure why, but maybe she couldn't (8) *tolerate* his bad manners any longer. I can't (9) *think of* any other reasons. They've had to (10) *cancel* the wedding.

Vocabulary: personal qualities

6 Use the words in the box to finish the second sentence of each pair so that it has the same meaning as the first sentence.

> encourages   brave   talented   dedicated
> determined   brilliant   involved   inspired

1 I played a part in the sports club.
  I was _____ in the sports club.
2 My mother was a great gardener. Her example made me want to be a gardener.
  She _____ me to become a gardener.
3 Sandra is good at singing, drawing, basketball and French.
  She is quite _____.
4 Jessie has a lot of courage. She isn't frightened of anything!
  She is really _____.
5 Lucy never stops trying. She never gives up.
  She is very _____.
6 My grandfather spent his whole life caring for animals.
  He _____ his life to animals.
7 My teacher makes us want to do our best.
  He _____ us to do our best.
8 Javier is a genius at maths.
  He is _____ at maths.

Vocabulary: memory and the senses

7 <u>Underline</u> the sentence endings which are not possible.

1 I love the sound
  A of rain.   **B** like a drum.
  C of children playing.
2 Can you remind me
  A to call Judy?   **B** of my friend?
  C to send that email?
3 This food tastes
  A like cheese.   **B** delicious.   **C** a type of fruit.
4 I've lost
  A the taste of apples.   **B** my watch.
  C some money.
5 That reminds me of
  A my grandmother.   **B** go home.
  C last weekend.
6 She doesn't like
  A the feel of wool.   **B** feeling of stone.
  C feeling tired.
7 It sounds
  A like a great book.   **B** fantastic.
  C of England.
8 Don't forget
  A buying milk.   **B** your towel.
  C to send me a postcard.
9 I can't remember
  A anything.   **B** my neighbour.   **C** of that film.
10 You look
  A a model.   **B** very beautiful.
  C like my sister.

Writing: thank you letters

8 Complete the phrases and sentences with words from the box. There are four extra words in the box.

> for   now   look   stay   soon   were
> was   helping   to   had   Best   of

1 Thanks a lot letting me stay.
2 wishes,
3 We forward to working with you.
4 I am writing thank you for all your hard work.
5 Thank you for me last weekend.
6 I a great time.
7 I hope to see you.
8 Your efforts appreciated.

Answer key

Unit 1 Friends

Lesson 1.1
Vocabulary: verbs, adjectives, prepositions
1 **1** keep in touch **2** a good sense of humour **3** ex-girlfriend **4** friend of a friend **5** get to know her **6** colleagues **7** have a lot in common **8** stranger, enjoyed his company **9** best friend **10** lost touch

2 **1** in **2** about **3** about **4** on **5** at **6** in **7** on **8** to

Grammar: auxiliary verbs
3a **1** Are you good at sports? **2** Has he got any brothers or sisters? **3** How old are they? **4** Do you like studying German? **5** Have you been to America? **6** Have you seen your boss today? **7** Did you go to the shops yesterday?

b **1** Yes, I am./No, I'm not. **2** Yes, he has./No, he hasn't. **3** Possible answer: 30 years old. **4** Yes, I do./No, I don't. **5** Yes, I have./No, I haven't. **6** Yes, I have./No, I haven't. **7** Yes, I did./No I didn't.

4a **1** What sports are you interested in? **2** Have you been skiing recently? **3** Does she like listening to music? **4** Did Mozart play the violin? **5** Did your parents enjoy the concert last night? **6** Did you speak to Frances yesterday? **7** Has Clara had her baby yet? **8** Were you born in Turin?

b **a** 3 **b** 8 **c** 6 **d** 5 **e** 4 **f** 1 **g** 7 **h** 2

Pronunciation
5a **1** nineteen point five **2** forty-seven percent **3** three hours and fifteen minutes **4** six thousand, one hundred and fifty-six **5** seventy-two point nine percent **6** one hundred and eighty

b **1** 8.967 **2** 92% **3** 645 **4** 27% **5** 3,642 **6** €410

Reading
6 **3** is the best title

7 **1** F **2** T **3** F **4** T **5** F **6** T **7** T

8 The average man or woman (line 9)
tend to (line 11)
generally (line 15)
usually (line 22)

Lesson 1.2
Vocabulary: computers
1 **1** message **2** research **3** down **4** download **5** online **6** website **7** delete **8** access

Grammar: Present Simple vs Present Continuous
2 **1** isn't raining **2** Correct **3** goes **4** is boiling **5** is getting **6** Correct **7** Are you using **8** We're staying **9** is trying **10** Correct

3 **1** 's/is getting **2** finish/takes **3** 's/is getting **4** Do you always listen… **5** 'm/am living **6** 're/are waiting **7** is **8** don't enjoy **9** go **10** 's/is playing

Writing
4 **1g** … and it was great to hear all your news. **2c** I'm sorry I haven't been in touch for such a long time, **3j** … but I'm very busy in my new job. **4d** My company is buying a factory in China, **5e** … so I have to travel a lot. **6a** It is very hard work **7h** … but I am enjoying it. **8i** Are you coming to Rico's wedding? **9b** I hope so **10f** … because it would be great to see you there.
(Alternative order: g, c, j, a, h, d, e, I, b, f)

Listening
5a **2** email relationships

b **1** b **2** b **3** a **4** a **5** a **6** b **7** b **8** a

Lesson 1.3
Grammar: Present Simple vs Past Simple
1 **1** have always admired **2** hasn't got married **3** has spent **4** has done **5** has learnt **6** has gone **7** have always wanted **8** flew **9** met **10** hasn't taught

2 **1** He has been a lawyer since 2002. **2** My parents have kept dogs since I was six years old. **3** She has been in Paris since last Tuesday. **4** I have known them for two years. **5** She has had that car for five years. **6** Alice has gone to the bank. **7** They have been married for 25 years. **8** They have worked (/ have been working) together since 2004.

Vocabulary: *for* and *since*
3 **1** ✓ **2** ✓ **3** I haven't had a cigarette *for* three weeks! **4** I've known Julia *since* we went to university. **5** I've lived here *for* ten years. **6** ✓ **7** Have you been here *for* a long time? **8** I've had a bad cold *since* last weekend. **9** ✓ **10** I haven't eaten anything *since* nine o'clock this morning.

Pronunciation
4

/ae/ apple	/ə/ company
athletics	can
happened	cigarette
cat	advice
	musicians
	have
	arrived
	comfortable

Reading
5 B

6 **1** No, he hasn't. **2** Yes, he did. **3** 1: the fact that his mother died; 2: the criticism he received from his brother and the media; 3: his new car. **4** His car. **5** Yes. **6** No.

Review and consolidation unit 1

Vocabulary
1 **1** website **2** best friends **3** lost **4** belong **5** keen **6** about **7** access **8** ex-girlfriend **9** get **10** strangers **11** common

Auxiliary verbs
2 **1** Do you live in Thailand? **2** Did you see the James Bond film last night? **3** When is Sal going on holiday?/When does Sal go on holiday? **4** What sports are you interested in? **5** Do you enjoy studying? **6** Have you forgotten your books? **7** Does Tim like working for IBM? **8** Are you happy in your new flat? **9** Did George G win the election? **10** Have you passed all your exams?

3 **1** am **2** he does **3** haven't **4** can **5** it is **6** they did **7** she is **8** they do **9** I have **10** he/she doesn't

Present Simple, Present Continuous, Present Perfect
4 **1** use **2** fly **3** do **4** are **5** doesn't seem **6** 've just finished **7** 's talking **8** 'm trying **9** 've always enjoyed **10** can't remember

for/since
5 **1** for **2** since **3** since **4** for **5** since **6** for **7** since **8** for **9** since **10** since

6 **1** I've *known* her for a long time. We went to school together. **2** 'Have you spoken to the manager?' 'Yes, I *did* it this morning.' **3** When *did they* get married? **4** We haven't *been* in touch *for* a long time. **5** When did you *start* working together? **6** I've never *watched* that programme. **7** It's the funniest book I've *ever* read. **8** She *has* had a hair cut. **9** I've just *started* to learn Tai Kwando. **10** I haven't *signed* the contract yet.

7 **1** Have/been **2** went **3** Did/enjoy **4** thought **5** Do/play **6** 'm/am **7** have/played **8** started **9** Do/want **10** sounds

Phrasal verbs
8 **1** up **2** brought **3** take **4** told **5** got **6** looked **7** on **8** up **9** into **10** joined

Prepositiuonal/phrasal verbs

9 **1** told **2** over **3** up **4** after **5** up **6** up **7** grew **8** on
9 in **10** after

Unit 2 Media

Lesson 2.1
Vocabulary: newspapers

1 **1** front page **2** interview **3** main story **4** review section
5 journalists **6** Online news
2

```
c e s e c t i o n s
e d   h
l i n t e r v i e w
e t   a
b o   d a i l y a
r r   l   d
i a r t i c l e v
t f r o n t p a g e
y   e   r
j o u r n a l i s t
```

1 journalist **2** front page **3** headline **4** article **5** celebrity
6 advert **7** interview **8** sections **9** daily **10** editor

Grammar: passive

3 **1** are written by **2** was made by **3** was organised by
4 been fixed **5** was signed **6** are switched off **7** be found
8 has been contacted

4 **1** be delivered **2** be answered **3** was told **4** be sent
5 is printed

How to …

5 **1** What **2** In **3** opinion **4** sure **5** reckon **6** so
7 depends **8** neither **9** Definitely

Reading

6 **a** **1** editors **2** gossip about famous people **3** fewer than 30%
b **2**
c **1** F **2** T **3** F **4** T **5** F **6** T

Lesson 2.2
Vocabulary: TV programmes

1 **1** microphone **2** quiz show **3** contestants **4** chat shows
5 documentary **6** soap **7** audience **8** newsreaders

How to …

2 **1 A:** What's the problem?
B: It's my computer. It isn't working properly.
A: Try switching it off.
B: I've tried that.
2 A: What's the matter?
B: It's my son's toy car. It keeps stopping.
A: Have the batteries run out?
B: Oh yes, you're right!
3 A: What's wrong with the lift?
B: It's out of order.
A: Shall I call the engineers?
B: I've just called them.

Grammar: *who, whose, which, where*

3 **1** … whose wife won the lottery. **2** … who are always honest.
3 … where we stayed last year. **4** … that makes jewellery.
5 … where you can surf all year. **6** … who designed my house.
7 … which looks best on you. **8** … whose films always make money.

4 **1** who/F **2** which/F **3** whose/T **4** where/T **5** who/F
6 which/T **7** whose/T **8** which/T

Reading

5 **a** **1** B **2** A **3** B **4** C **5** C **6** A
b **1** hackers **2** came out **3** star reporter **4** fired **5** insisted
6 under pressure

Lesson 2.3
Vocabulary: regular and irregular verbs

1 **1** woke up **2** drew **3** inherited **4** flew **5** caught
6 fought **7** forgot **8** cost **9** escaped **10** cut

Pronunciation

2 **1** c **2** d **3** b **4** d **5** a **6** c
3 **1** A: 3 B: 4 **2** A: 3 B: 4 **3** A: 4 B: 3 **4** A: 3 B: 3 **5** A: 3 B: 3

Grammar: Past Simple and Past Continuous

4 **1** was driving **2** didn't understand **3** was playing
4 were resting **5** went **6** did you know **7** were you doing
8 were talking

5 **1** were looking **2** found **3** went **4** was **5** were worrying
6 spent **7** was brushing **8** said **9** stopped **10** was driving

6 **1** stole/wasn't looking **2** didn't know/were **3** didn't hear/were
listening **4** was driving/saw **5** didn't take/was **6** met/were
skiing

Listening

7a **1** fat **2** homes **3** taxi driver **4** rock star (Lee Santana)
b **1** 900 schoolchildren aged 11 to 15 **2** Hamburgers, chips,
chocolate, fizzy soft drinks **3** Shopping area and car park
4 Next year **5** A husband and wife **6** A London hospital
7 In a small art gallery (in Manchester) **8** Extremely happy

Review and consolidation unit 2

Past Simple, Past Continuous and Passive

1 **1** was spent **2** was working **3** did you realise
4 was stopped **5** didn't go **6** was discovered **7** were you
talking **8** were staying **9** didn't know **10** be eaten

2a **1** d **2** f **3** b **4** a **5** h **6** c **7** g **8** e
b 1, 5, 2, 4, 6, 7, 3, 8
c Past Continuous: was trying, was carrying, was wearing, was
working, was counting
Passive: wasn't caught, was captured, was written

Defining relative clauses

3 **1** Graceland is the place where Elvis Presley died. **2** Franz Kafka
was the writer who wrote a story about a man who became an insect.
3 St Petersburg is the city which used to be called Leningrad.
4 Rodin was the sculptor who made *The Thinker*. **5** *Titanic* is the
famous film which cost $200,000,000 to make. **6** Malibu is the
beach in California where hundreds of celebrities live. **7** Vivaldi
was the composer whose most famous work was *The Four Seasons*.
8 Istanbul is the city which is built on two continents – Europe
and Asia.

4 **1** who was given **2** which (or that) are told **3** whose paintings
are sold **4** where I was born **5** which (or that) can be used
6 whose bags have been **7** who must be stopped

Irregular verbs

5 **1** A **2** D **3** D **4** B **5** C **6** A **7** B **8** B **9** B **10** C

How to …

6a **1** *In* my opinion, we should buy the black sofa, not the blue one.
2 What *do* you think of that new Bruce Willis film? **3** You think we
should leave at 8.00, but I'm not sure *about* that. **4** She said we
could get in to the club free, but I don't think *so*. **5** I'd love to go
to the beach, but it depends *on* the weather. **6** What's *the* matter
with your TV? The picture isn't very good, is it? **7** If your computer
isn't working, try turning *it* off and on again. **8** The photocopier is
out *of* order again. **9** The problem with your printer is that it's run
out *of* paper! **10** If the microwave breaks down again, call us and
we can fix *it* immediately.

b **1** e **2** i **3** b **4** j **5** a **6** f **7** g **8** c **9** h **10** d

Vocabulary
7a

People	Types of TV programme	Things in a newspaper
cameraman, journalist, newsreader, celebrity, editor, contestant, presenter	documentary, quiz show, soap, chat show	headline, the front page, review section, article, main story, advertisement

b 1 review section **2** documentary **3** soap **4** journalist
5 contestant **6** celebrity **7** advertisement **8** the front page
9 presenter **10** article

Unit 3 Lifestyle

Lesson 3.1
Vocabulary: home
1 1 fireplace **2** wooden **3** good view **4** condition **5** lift
6 ceilings **7** attic **8** cellar **9** cramped **10** drive

Grammar: Present continuous vs *going to*/*will* for future
2 1 I'm going to change **2** I'll have **3** I'll show **4** We're going
5 I'll do **6** I'm going (to go)/I'll get

3 1 I need some fresh air. I think *I'll go* for a walk. **2** *Are* you
seeing Jack at the weekend? **3** What time *is* Susannah coming?
4 We*'re (are)* going to Berlin at the end of the month. **5** They've
changed their minds. They're *not* going to Thailand any more, they
are *going* to Greece. **6** Are you coming to the concert too? Great
– we*'ll (will)* see you there then. **7** He doesn't like the new job so
I don't think he*'ll* stay there for very long. **8** 'What are your plans
for supper?' 'I*'m (am)* cooking pizza.'

Writing: a formal letter
4 (1) <u>Dear</u> Mr Smith,
(2) <u>I am writing to complain about</u> the accommodation that your
company provides.
(3) <u>According to your website</u>, the apartments are all modern and
in good condition. (4) <u>In fact</u>, the apartment I stayed in was built in
the 1970s, and needed work doing to it. The floors in the kitchen and
bathroom were broken and dirty. (5) <u>In addition to this</u>, the washing
machine was not working.
(6) <u>I was also very disappointed</u> to find that the apartment was a long
way from the beach, and not 'within ten minutes walk' as specified in
the brochure.
I had to move to another apartment, which took me time and cost
me money. I paid over 300 Euros as a deposit on your flat and now
(7) <u>I expect to receive a full refund</u>.
(8) <u>I would also like</u> you to change the information on your website
and in your brochures.
(9) <u>I look forward to receiving a satisfactory reply</u>.
(10) <u>Yours sincerely</u>
Miguel Rodrigues

Reading
5a

	Jean-Marc, Felicity and Yannick	Pat, John and Sally
Where is their house?	South of France	Bongor, UK
How many bedrooms are there?	6	10
Other features of the house/area	swimming pool, vineyards, large gardens	seaside town
How much money does the hotel/bed and breakfast make?	€50,000	€30,000
How do they spend their time?	swimming, eating, playing golf and enjoying the Mediterranean lifestyle	working: shopping, cooking, cleaning
What do they want to get from the house swap?	useful work experience for their daughter Yannick	to see how different life could be in France

b It is different because these couples are swapping their houses
and their businesses too.

Listening
6a 1 Yes, it was a success for Pat. **2** No, it wasn't a success
for Jean-Marc.

b 1 It was like a honeymoon because they stayed in a beautiful villa,
and there wasn't a lot of work to do. **2** She had to make coffee.
3 They travelled and went sailing.

c 4 They lived underground, in two small rooms in the basement.
5 He thought the traditional breakfast was unhealthy. **6** No, it
wasn't a success because she didn't learn anything useful.
7 No, they wouldn't.

Lesson 3.2
Vocabulary: adjectives for describing place
1a modern – historic   ugly – picturesque   tiny – enormous
clean – polluted   dull – lively

b 1 peaceful **2** historic **3** enormous **4** polluted **5** lively
6 picturesque **7** modern **8** dull

Grammar: comparatives and superlatives
2 1 more peaceful **2** more expensive **3** heavier **4** more
modern **5** nearer **6** smaller **7** worse **8** longer
3 1 the best **2** more expensive than **3** the hottest **4** more
relaxed **5** most beautiful **6** the liveliest **7** more romantic
8 busier

Reading
4 1 ✓ **2** – **3** ✓ **4** – **5** ✓
5 1 g **2** e **3** f **4** b **5** a **6** c **7** d
6 1 C **2** B **3** B **4** C **5** A **6** B **7** A **8** B

Lesson 3.3
Vocabulary: compound nouns
1 1 alarm clock **2** washing machine **3** air conditioning
4 central heating **5** mobile phone **6** burglar alarm
7 answering machine **8** video player

Pronunciation: compound nouns
2a In compound nouns the stress is usually on the *first* part.
Sometimes, it is on both parts.

b **credit** card   **table** tennis   **T-**shirt   **science fiction**   **ear**ring
sunglasses   **traffic** lights   **mother tongue**   **parking** meter
dining room   **baby-**sitter   **brother-**in-law   **first aid**

Science fiction, *mother tongue* and *first aid* have the stress on
both parts.

Grammar: future probability
3 1 We'll probably see you at the party. **2** He might not want to
come. **3** They may meet us at the airport. **4** Mrs Simmons might
call about the contract. **5** Could you book a table for eight o'clock,
please? **6** Do you think you might buy the house? **7** I probably
won't be back until next week.

4 1 won't arrive **2** 'll rain **3** might come **4** 'll probably need
5 may have **6** Could **7** won't need **8** might become

Formal phone calls
5 ☐1 Good morning. Sonny Korean Banks Ltd. Can I ~~to~~ help you?
☐5 Thank you. I'll just put you through. ~~In~~ One moment.
☐8 Certainly ~~so~~.
☐4 Yes, this is Jasper Coffin. I'm returning ~~for~~ his call.
☐2 Yes, I'd ~~very~~ like to speak to Mr Allen please.
☐6 I'm afraid he's on the other line at the moment. Would you like
to call ~~he~~ back later?
☐3 May I ask who's calling ~~me~~ please?
☐9 Could he call me at the office, on 0052 427 9835? I'll be here
~~always~~ until seven p.m. Thank you. Goodbye.
☐7 Could I ~~to~~ leave a message?
☐8 Goodbye.

Reading
6a How your house will change **C**   Predictions that were wrong **A**
Your clothes will know where you are **D**   Changes in information
technology **B**

b 1 F **2** T **3** T **4** F **5** T **6** F

C **1** trend **2** settings **3** use-by date **4** public transport
5 reminder **6** laptop

Review and consolidation unit 3

Lifestyle

1 **1** block **2** floor **3** area **4** hectic **5** view **6** suburbs
7 old-fashioned **8** playground **9** lively **10** clubbing
11 outskirts **12** balcony

Present Continuous *going to*/*will* for future

2 **1** **A:** Are you going to Spain again this year? **B:** No. We*'re* going
to Greece instead. **2** I don't think I*'ll* go to the cinema tonight
because I'm too tired. **3** Who is meet*ing* us at the airport?
4 We*'re* getting married in June. **5** **A:** Have you decided which one
you want to buy yet? **B:** Yes. I will ~~to~~ take this one please.
6 We're going *to* see Andrea tomorrow. Do you want to come with us?
7 **A:** I'm really hungry. **B:** OK. I*'ll* ~~'m going to~~ make us some lunch
now. **8** **A:** What are you doing at the weekend? **B:** We*'re going*
~~will go~~ to visit my mother-in-law. (or *we're visiting*) **9** ~~Do~~ *Will* you
~~will~~ come with us to the office? **10** Can you tell Jonathan I*'ll* see
him later? **11** ~~Do~~ *Are* you coming to Madrid to watch the football?
12 Sue is ~~leave~~ *leaving* for Brazil and I'm not going to see her any more.

Comparatives, superlatives, adjectives

3 **1** more picturesque than **2** the liveliest **3** most unspoilt
4 most peaceful **5** uglier **6** the dullest **7** more modern
8 less polluted **9** cleaner **10** more touristy

Compound nouns

4 **1** I didn't wake up in time because I forgot to set my *alarm clock*.
2 It's cold in here. Let's turn on the *central heating*. **3** When she
opened the door the *burglar alarm* went off and soon the police
arrived. **4** I left a message on your *mobile phone*. **5** I don't have
anything to wear because my clothes are all in the *washing machine*.
6 Can you set the *video recorder* to record this film at nine o'clock?
7 My new car has *air-conditioning* which I use when it is really hot.
8 Can I borrow your *mobile phone*? I need to call my office.

Future probability

5 **1** We'll probably see you in the restaurant. **2** Do you think
she might say 'Yes'? **3** I think I'm going to be late for the lesson.
4 You definitely won't need to change money. **5** They'll certainly
ask you for your passport. **6** We may not get an answer until
tomorrow. **7** I'll definitely call her again in the morning.
8 She could arrive at any time. **9** Helga probably won't go
to Russia next year. **10** He might not accept the job he was
offered. **11** We probably won't stay for long. **12** I certainly won't
contact them until I know the answer.

Prefixes and suffixes

6 **1** overworked **2** ex-girlfriend **3** rearrange **4** messy
5 unbelievable **6** peaceful **7** unusual **8** misunderstanding
9 creative **10** used

How to …

7a **1** Good morning. Casa Bruno. *Can* I help you? **2** *Could* he call
me back? My mobile number is 01797 202345 **3** Hello. I'd *like* to
speak to Mr Marconi, please. **4** I'll *put* you through. *One* moment.
5 Yes, *it's* Gabriella Saltini. I'm calling *about* the new designs.
6 May I *ask* who's calling? **7** Can I *leave* a message? **8** I'm afraid
he's *not* here at the moment. Would you like to *call* back later?
9 Certainly. What's *the* message?

b 1 3 6 5 4 8 7 9 2

8 **1** Diego is not as tall as Juan. **2** New York is cheaper than
London. **3** Glasgow is more touristy than before. **4** Florence is
the most picturesque city. **5** San Francisco is not as polluted as Los
Angeles. **6** Singapore is one of the cleanest cities . **7** Shanghai
has got busier recently. **8** The west coast of the island is unspoilt.
9 Due to terrorist activity, life in cities is not as safe as before.
10 The new gallery is more modern than the old one.

Unit 4 Wealth

Lesson 4.1

Vocabulary: time and money collocations

1 **1** ~~thought~~ **2** ~~time~~ **3** ~~hobby~~ **4** ~~our time~~ **5** ~~chance to spare~~
6 ~~sometime~~

2 **1** broken up **2** dropped out **3** work out **4** ran out
5 picked up **6** catch up **7** ended up

3 **1** Do you know the answer? I can't *work it out*. **2** When I was
living in Germany I *picked up* some German. **3** I hated university
so I *dropped out*. **4** I missed some lessons but I *caught up* quickly
by working at night. **5** He was a brilliant young scientist and he
ended up working for the government. **6** Unfortunately, Lisa and
I *broke up* last week. **7** Oh no! We've *run out of* milk. Can you go
and buy some?

Grammar: question tags

4a **1** have you **2** have you **3** did you **4** have you **5** are you
6 didn't you

b **1** d **2** e **3** c **4** f **5** b **6** a

5 **1** c **2** f **3** j **4** h **5** i **6** d **7** k **8** a **9** b **10** e
11 l **12** g

Listening

6 ☐1 her job ☐2 Internet fraud ☐3 shopping online
☐4 investing your money ☐5 'Phishing' ☐6 features of
secure websites

2 **1** She tells the public what's happening and explains how to
stop fraud. **2** It's impersonal: criminals can steal money without
ever meeting their victims. **3** They are a dangerous sign. **4** You
should never give bank account numbers and passwords **5** It's a
way for criminals to steal money online. You receive an email that
says it's from a famous company. It asks you urgently for your details
(passwords, etc.) and uses this information to rob your money.
6 The letters 'https' (at the top of the screen), and an image of
a lock or key (at the bottom of the screen) show that a website
is probably safe.

Lesson 4.2

Vocabulary: personal qualities

1

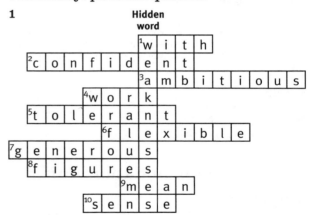

Hidden word: weaknesses

Grammar: modal verbs

2 **1** You must come here now. **2** I've finished. What should I do
now? **3** You mustn't smoke in the office. **4** You don't have to wear
a suit, but you can if you want to. **5** Shouldn't you be at home now?
6 Do I have to buy a ticket? **7** She doesn't have to clean her room
every day; only at weekends. **8** Our boss has to be in the office at
seven a.m. **9** I must go to the station now. **10** We don't have to
walk. We can take the car.

3 **1** should **2** have to **3** should **4** mustn't **5** mustn't
6 should **7** don't have to **8** don't have to

Writing

4 Dear Mr Mishovsky, ☐1

I am writing to invite you to our annual dinner in the Atrium
Restaurant on 19th July. ☐2

The dinner will begin at 8.00. ☐3

I have enclosed a form with further information which you can also
use to reserve places. ☐4

We look forward to hearing from you. ☐5

Yours sincerely,

Miles Broom ☐6

Dear Miles Broom, [7]

Thank you for the invitation to the annual dinner. [8]

I am afraid I am unable to attend due to a business trip in Switzerland. [9]

I do hope the evening goes well. [10]

Yours sincerely,

Reuben Mishovsky [11]

Pronunciation

5 **1** I **have** to **work**. **2** We **should** go to Po**land**. **3** Do I **have** to **sing**? **4** I **must** get **home**. **5** You don't **have** to **leave**. **6** You **should**n't do **that**. **7** They **must**n't drive **there**. **8** It doesn't **have** to be **big**.

Reading

6a **1** T **2** F **3** T **4** T **5** F **6** F **7** F **8** T

b **1** B **2** A **3** B **4** A **5** B **6** B

Lesson 4.3
Vocabulary: opposites

1 **1** advertisements **2** succeed **3** fail **4** buyers **5** respond **6** reward **7** buy

2 **1** advertises **2** success **3** sell **4** product **5** produces **6** advertisements **7** consumes **8** response **9** rewards **10** buyer

Pronunciation: word stress

3 **1** ad**ver**tisement **2** **ad**vertise **3** res**pond** **4** re**ward** **5** **fail**ure **6** suc**ceed** **7** suc**cess** **8** **pun**ishment

Grammar: first conditional

4 **1** As soon as **2** If **3** Unless **4** When **5** If **6** Unless **7** If **8** When **9** If **10** When

5 **1** e **2** b **3** c **4** g **5** h **6** a **7** d **8** f

6 **1** A: won't be/I finish   B: you know/will you phone **2** A: will you go/take   B: I have/will visit   **3** A: graduate/will you become   B: find/won't be   **4** A: will be/we turn   B: don't find/will die

Reading

7a C is the best heading.

b **1** B **2** D **3** A **4** C **5** B **6** D

c **1** T **2** T **3** F **4** F **5** T **6** F

Review and consolidation unit 4

Question tags

1 **1** It's a horrible day, isn't it? **2** You've lost weight, haven't you? **3** This radio show isn't very interesting, is it? **4** You ate my last chocolate, didn't you? **5** You will write to me, won't you? **6** You haven't seen my sunglasses, have you? **7** You don't eat meat, do you? **8** You can drive, can't you? **9** She was wonderful, wasn't she? **10** You still run every day, don't you?

Question tags and modals of obligation

2 **1** We should bring flowers, shouldn't we? **2** You don't have to freeze this food, do you? **3** I need to send Judith an email, don't I? **4** We mustn't write in the book, must we? **5** They shouldn't arrive so late, should they? **6** He has to go to class now, doesn't he? **7** She doesn't have to wear a hat, does she? **8** I must invite Samuel, mustn't I? **9** You have to memorise the password, don't you? **10** None of us should be worried, should we?

Modals of obligation/first conditional

3 **1** If we don't **2** as soon as **3** don't have to **4** I won't be **5** should phone **6** mustn't play **7** doesn't have to take **8** will come **9** shouldn't eat **10** as soon as

4 **1** buy/won't **2** If/won't **3** pass/will **4** Will you/know **5** If/won't **6** will/join **7** will/put **8** When/will organise **9** Unless/won't **10** Won't you/don't

Phrasal verbs and time/money collocations

5 **1** ~~our relationship~~ **2** ~~the lesson~~ **3** ~~quickly~~ **4** ~~my errors~~ **5** ~~life~~ **6** ~~her time~~ **7** ~~finally~~ **8** ~~my shoes~~ **9** ~~opportunity~~ **10** ~~the car~~

Vocabulary

6 reward/punishment   time to spare/not enough time   success/failure   buyer/seller   produce/consume   use money wisely/waste money   not worth the money/good value for money   respond to an advertisement/advertise

1 time to spare **2** punishment **3** good value for money **4** advertise **5** consume **6** reward **7** success **8** not worth the money **9** waste money **10** not enough time

Confusing words

7 **1** B **2** A **3** B **4** B **5** A **6** A **7** B **8** A **9** B **10** A

How to ...

8a **1** I'm having a party on Friday. **2** Would you like to come? **3** I am writing to invite you to the Annual Mason's Ball. **4** I've attached a map, so you can find my place easily! **5** Come anytime after 8.oo. **6** Dinner will be served at 8.30. **7** I'd love to come to your party! **8** I will be pleased to attend the Choral Society's AGM. **9** Sorry, I can't make it because I've got another party to go to. **10** I am afraid I am unable to attend due to a previous engagement.

b **1** I **2** I **3** F **4** I **5** I **6** F **7** I **8** F **9** I **10** F

Unit 5 Spare time

Lesson 5.1
Vocabulary: free time activities

1 **Across** **1** gloves **4** karate **5** squash **6** aerobics **8** court **9** gardening **10** fishing **12** gym

Down **2** volleyball **3** opponent **5** surfing **7** cycling **11** net

Grammar: Present Perfect Simple vs Continuous

2 **1** finished **2** been watching **3** been working **4** been going **5** known **6** been practising **7** seen

3 **1** have known **2** have been looking for **3** have been running **4** have been playing **5** haven't heard **6** has she been learning **7** have you invited

Pronunciation: contractions

4 **1** A **2** B **3** A **4** A **5** B **6** B **7** B **8** A

How to ...

5 **1** Why don't we go to the cinema? **2** I'm not sure about that. **3** So wouldn't it be better to eat at home? **4** Shall we try a museum?

Reading and listening

6a **1** T **2** F **3** F **4** F **5** T **6** T

b **1** announced **2** bank **3** magnificent **4** hovered **5** froze **6** barked

c **1** A **2** C **3** B **4** C **5** B **6** A **7** C

Lesson 5.2
Vocabulary: books and films

1a **1** dubbed **2** sequel **3** published **4** chapter **5** star **6** title **7** plot **8** setting **9** writer **10** performance **11** soundtrack

b The key word is description.

Pronunciation

2 **1** A and B **2** B and D **3** A and C **4** B and D **5** B and C **6** A and C

Grammar: gerunds vs infinitives

3 **1** to work **2** to have **3** to discuss **4** to read **5** to find **6** starting **7** speaking **8** to read **9** to write **10** to look **11** to enjoy **12** to read

4 **1** playing **2** writing **3** to paint **4** to play **5** to be **6** to beat **7** to have **8** studying

How to ...

5 **1** characters **2** by **3** about **4** set **5** stars **6** thing **7** act **8** plot **9** recommend **10** sequel

Listening

6

Speaker	Name of film/ comic book	Opinion
1 Denise	*X-Men*	The film was *better* than the comic book. She loved the *action*.
2 Ahmed	*Spiderman*	He preferred the *comic*. The star looked too *young*.
3 Eliza	*Batman*	The comic is dark but the film is *funny*. She loved the performance of *Jack Nicholson*.
4 Glynn	*Superman*	He likes the comic and the film. He also loves the *soundtrack*. He doesn't like *the sequels* as much.

Lesson 5.3
Vocabulary: food and eating out

1a

```
(d  e  s  s  e  r  t) l
(b) d  t (p  l  a  t  e)
(o (n  a  p  k  i  n) g
 w  h  r (c  u  p) k  l
(l) c (t  i  p) b  n  a
 s  g  e (m  e  a  l) s
(s  e  r  v  i  c  e) s
```

b 1 cup **2** service **3** starter **4** meal

a tip **b** glass **c** dessert **d** bowl

c 1 b **2** a **3** d **4** c

Writing: a summary

2 1 who is six years old **2** when **3** after **4** which is delicious **5** eventually **6** which is based on Joanne Harris's novel **7** while

Grammar: countable vs uncountable

3 1 C **2** A **3** D **4** B **5** B **6** C **7** A **8** D

4 1 many **2** couple **3** few **4** little **5** many of **6** a piece of **7** few **8** little

How to ...

5 1 It's near the main square. **2** It specialises in Thai food. **3** Yes, it's very fresh. **4** The waiters are very friendly. **5** Yes, the service is a little slow. **6** It is quite expensive. **7** It's worth a visit.

Reading

6a 1 C **2** B **3** E **4** D **5** A

b 1 C and D **2** B and D **3** A and E **4** C and D **5** A and D **6** B and D

Review and consolidation unit 5

Present Perfect Simple and Continuous

1 1 Haven't you finished **2** Have you been eating **3** Have you been reading **4** I've asked **5** I've been studying **6** has been **7** have been skiing **8** We've stopped **9** have been looking **10** have used

Verb patterns and uncountable/uncountable

2 1 cooking/a lot of **2** to find out/any **3** to talk/some **4** meeting/so many **5** to tell/– **6** to go/too much **7** writing/ many **8** looking after/– **9** running/– **10** to eat/an

Verb patterns

3 1 C **2** B **3** C **4** A **5** B **6** C **7** B **8** A **9** B **10** A

Present Perfect Simple and Continuous, and countable/uncountable nouns

4 1 She's been studying the subject for a couple of years. **2** I've heard a lot of interesting stories about Mark. **3** Some of you haven't been working hard enough. **4** I've been coming here for many years. **5** He hasn't spent much time in Brazil. **6** A few of us have stayed in Prague before. **7** She's been taking too many days off work. **8** He's been trying to find some information. **9** I haven't seen you for a few days. **10** My mother has been doing a lot of gardening today.

Vocabulary

5 a = aerobics b = bowl c = chapter d = dubbed e = exercise f = fishing g = gardening h = hard i = instructor j = jogging k = karate l = light m = main character n = napkin o = opponent p = plot q = quite r = rough s = starter t = tip u = uncountable v = volleyball w = wide

Explaining what you mean

6a 1 It's a type *of* machine you use for cooking things fast. **2** It's *a kind of* game that uses pieces like kings and queens. **3** It's the *stuff* you find on the ground after a freezing night. **4** It's something you use for *boiling* water to make coffee (**or** *to boil*). **5** They are made *of* rubber and you put them on your wheels. **6** They are usually *rectangular* and you put pictures inside them. **7** It's a cold place in Europe that is absolutely *huge*. **8** It's a *sticky* type of tape that you can use to attach paper to a wall. **9** It's a square, *hard* type of bread that you can eat with cheese. **10** You use this to wash yourself and smell good. It's very *smooth*.

b a 9 b 5 c 4 d 8 e 6 f 7 g 3 h 10 i l j 2

How to ...

7a 1 The service is *a little slow*. **2** The main *characters* are really interesting. **3** It was directed *by* Francis Ford Coppola. **4** It's worth *a visit*. **5** Wouldn't *it* be better to practise every day? **6** I've *been* doing this for about six years. **7** The food is beautifully *prepared*. **8** It's *set* in Chicago in the 1920s. **9** The *prices* are reasonable. **10** It's not really *worth* seeing. **11** I've *improved* a lot since I first started. **12** It specialises *in* modern French cuisine.

b 1 R **2** F **3** F **4** R **5** H **6** H **7** R **8** F **9** R **10** F **11** H **12** R

Unit 6 Holidays

Lesson 6.1
Vocabulary: travel

1 1 going **2** landmark **3** rainforest **4** sandy **5** historic **6** unforgettable **7** go **8** package **9** fun **10** local

Reading: Past Perfect

2 1 I had finished **2** He had run out of **3** We had never expected **4** Had it been

a 3 **b** 4 **c** 1 **d** 2

Grammar: Past Perfect vs Past Simple

3 1 Because he had forgotten his passport. **2** Because he had packed (a pair of) scissors. **3** Because he hadn't seen the No Smoking sign. **4** Because he hadn't booked (a room). **5** Because he hadn't put on sun cream. **6** Because he hadn't brought his/a camera. **7** Because he had lost his key. **8** Because he had missed his dog.

How to ...

4 1 shows **2** background **3** one **4** on **5** excited **6** been **7** Afterwards

Listening

5a 1 c **2** e **3** d **4** a **5** f **6** g **7** b

b *Student's own answers.*

c She mentions: **b** advice for people who want to be travel writers **d** how tourism has changed **e** how long she has been a travel writer

d 1 She feels that she's only just starting. **2** In the 1970s, over thirty years ago. **3** Normal people can now see more of the world. They don't have to be rich. **4** Tour guides can take you up the mountain, so you don't need any training. **5** Sandy Hill Pitman's guides carried her laptop computer, coffee machine and luxury food up Everest and she had fashion magazines delivered to the mountain. She is 'the bad side of modern tourism'. **6** She suggests that they should make time to write and they should look for details.

Lesson 6.2
Vocabulary: places to visit in a city
1a

a	r	t	g	a	l	l	e	r	y
j	d	f	c	a	s	t	l	e	f
m	u	s	e	u	m	f	p	c	o
a	s	h	o	p	s	g	a	h	u
r	s	e	c	a	x	l	r	u	n
k	l	e	s	l	v	a	k	r	t
e	c	u	f	a	t	k	m	c	a
t	a	d	t	c	r	e	o	h	i
c	a	t	h	e	d	r	a	l	n

b **1** church, cathedral   **2** art gallery, museum   **3** shops, market   **4** lake, fountain   **5** castle, palace

Pronunciation: how to sound polite
2 Polite: 1, 3, 5, 6, 7   Impolite: 2, 4, 8

How to ...
3 **1** How much is a ticket to the city centre?   **2** What time does the palace close?   **3** Excuse me, do you know where the museum is?   **4** Can you tell me the way to the cathedral, please?   **5** Excuse me, is there a bank near here?   **6** Does this bus go to the art gallery?

Grammar: uses of *like*
4 **1** What's the flat like? Is it big?   **2** Would you like some help? I'm free at the moment.   **3** Your house looks like a museum. I love your old furniture.   **4** I like listening to music. My favourite band is The Fugees.   **5** What does your girlfriend look like? Is she tall and blonde? I think I saw her yesterday.   **6** What's that film like? I've heard it's very sad.   **7** What would you like to do this evening? There's a good film on at the cinema.   **8** What was the weather like? I hope it didn't rain and ruin your holiday.

5 **1** What's he like?   **2** Does John look like Pete?   **3** Do you like maths?   **4** What does the building look like?   **5** What was the concert like?   **6** Does your mother look like you?   **7** Would you like a cup of tea?   **8** What is the weather going to be like tomorrow?

Writing
6 **1** The first place to go is Princes Street.   **2** The Modern Art Museum is one of the best art galleries to visit.   **3** You mustn't miss Edinburgh Castle.   **4** If you enjoy traditional food, make sure you include a trip to Bannerman's Restaurant.   **5** Don't leave without seeing The Grassmarket.   **6** Finally, why not try some haggis?

Reading
7a Bhutan, Papua New Guinea and Florida Keys

b **1** dangerous weather – Tornado Alley   **2** a peaceful lifestyle – Bhutan   **3** killer sharks – Florida Keys, USA   **4** ancient tribes – rainforest, Papua New Guinea   **5** lots of space – Sahara Desert

c **1**A   **2**A   **3**B   **4**A   **5**A

Lesson 6.3
Vocabulary: adjectives to describe natural places
1 **1** desert   **2** range   **3** deep   **4** rocky   **5** tropical

Grammar: articles
2 *A* man sent himself in *a* wooden box from New York to Dallas because he thought it was *the* cheapest way to fly.

Charles McKinley, 25, missed his family but thought the flight home would be too expensive. *A* friend told him it would be cheaper to go as cargo. In fact, *the* cost of sending the wooden box was higher than *an* economy class seat.

After a 15-hour journey in which McKinley had no food or water, *the* box was delivered to his parents' home. McKinley surprised everybody by jumping out of the box. The delivery man called *the* police immediately, and McKinley was arrested.

3 **1** the, the   **2** –, the   **3** the, a   **4** the, The   **5** –, a   **6** the, the   **7** –, a   **8** –, the

Pronunciation
4 **1** **A:** I'm tired.   **B:** *Really*? You slept for ten hours!   **2** **A:** I was in hospital for six weeks.   **B:** How *awful*! Are you better now?   **3** **A:** I just passed my driving test.   **B:** That's *great*! Congratulations!   **4** **A:** It's going to rain tomorrow.   **B:** Oh *no*! I want to go to the beach.   **5** **A:** My father was a diplomat.   **B:** How *interesting*! Which countries?

How to ...
5 **1** Do you?   **2** Did he?   **3** Is it?   **4** Will you?   **5** Is there?   **6** Haven't they?   **7** Is she?   **8** Haven't you?

Reading
6a Travel agents might do all of these except 6: 'tell people which plane to get on'.

b The text mentions all of them except 4: 'find cheap holidays'.

c **1** F   **2** T   **3** F   **4** T   **5** F   **6** T

d **1** A   **2** B   **3** A   **4** B   **5** B

Review and consolidation unit 6

Past Perfect vs Past Simple
1 **1** A   **2** C   **3** C   **4** B   **5** B   **6** A   **7** C   **8** B

Past Perfect and articles
2 **1** had failed/the   **2** a/became   **3** the/didn't stay   **4** had broken/–   **5** –/started   **6** the/had already fallen   **7** hadn't recognised /the   **8** a/came   **9** an/had never seen   **10** –/went

Uses of *like*
3 **1** What's Warsaw like?   **2** Would they like some milk?   **3** I wouldn't like to be famous.   **4** What did Johnny look like?   **5** It tastes like meat.   **6** What will robots be like in the future? / What will robots of the future be like?   **7** I've never liked rock music.   **8** Is Spanish grammar like Portuguese grammar?   **9** Luisa looks like her big sister, Daniela.   **10** Mum, what was life like in the 1960s?

Articles and uses of *like*
4a **1** It's *a* small, pretty town in the south of England, famous for cider, a drink made with apples.   **2** They're tall and handsome, and *the* oldest one has *a* really good sense of humour.   **3** *Correct*   **4** Horses. I wanted to be *a* horse trainer when I was younger.   **5** It was a brilliant place. *The* owner was very friendly.   **6** *Correct*   **7** It's one of *the* biggest buildings in *the* city, and it's made of glass.   **8** Yes please. Actually, can I have *a* piece of toast?

b **1**c   **2**h   **3**f   **4**g   **5**e   **6**d   **7**b   **8**a

Vocabulary
5a

Travel expressions	Places to visit/see	Expressions with *get*
independent travel	landmark	to the airport
cruise	lake	back
package holiday	tropical rainforest	a taxi
camping holiday	sandy beach	directions
go on safari	castle	lost
sightseeing tour	rocky coastline	
	desert	

b **1** package   **2** safari   **3** taxi   **4** cruise   **5** lost   **6** landmark   **7** sightseeing   **8** back   **9** camping   **10** rainforest

6 **1** get married   **2** getting better   **3** getting back   **4** got on with   **5** get dressed   **6** got lost   **7** get to   **8** got bored   **9** get divorced   **10** get

How to ...
7 **1** Excuse me. Is *there* a post office near here?   **2** Can you tell *me* the way to the theatre, please?   **3** What time *does* the museum close?   **4** How *much* is a ticket to the city centre?   **5** Excuse me. Could you tell me *how* to get to Eve's Restaurant?   **6** Does this train go *to* the airport?   **7** Do you know how much a hire car costs per day?   **8** Can *you* recommend a good nightclub?

Unit 7 Education

Lesson 7.1
Vocabulary: education
1 1 made 2 doing 3 did 4 revising 5 from 6 do 7 get 8 take 9 going 10 got

2 1 thrown 2 perfect 3 learn 4 heart 5 making

Grammar: subject and object questions
3 1 Who took the keys? 2 What did Jonathan want to talk to me about? 3 Which office has Anna-Lisa moved to? 4 Which bus goes to the station? 5 Who asked you to be here at ten o'clock? 6 When did you arrive? 7 Who did you sell your car to? 8 Who would like (some) lunch? 9 What's/What has happened to the computer? 10 Who is buying the business?

4a 1 Which country held the 1990 World Cup? 2 Who won the Italian presidential election in 1997? 3 Who created the statue of David in Florence? 4 What destroyed the city of Pompeii? 5 Where does the Pope live? 6 Which city is built on 1300 small islands? 7 What do Italians usually eat for lunch? 8 Where did Christopher Columbus first sail from?

b 1 f 2 e 3 g 4 b 5 c 6 h 7 d 8 a

5 1 Who gave Mina my email address? 2 ✓ 3 Who does the book belong to? 4 Who invented the computer? 5 ✓ 6 ✓ 7 Where does Marianna live? 8 What happened at the meeting?

Reading
6 (Line 9) … people become frightened of them. *They fail to see them as part of the learning process.* In these kinds of environments …
(Line 20) … They experiment with all the buttons, just to see what will happen. *Then they restart the computer, and experiment again.* And they are learning …
(Line 28) … and we can see this often in successful professionals and leaders. *People who achieve great success then have more to lose when things go wrong.* So they start to worry …
(Line 30) … Don't let this happen to you. *Learn to talk about your mistakes, at work and at home.* See what opportunities …

7 Line 9: them – mistakes
Line 19: they – children
Line 27: this – the fear of success
Line 30: this – starting to worry and deciding not to take risks

8 1 bother 2 fall over 3 mispronounce 4 juggle 5 keys 6 draw outside the lines 7 take risks 8 opportunities

Lesson 7.2
Vocabulary: adjectives
1 1 fierce 2 pale 3 inspiring 4 patient 5 boring 6 knowledgeable 7 understanding 8 open-minded

2 1 She often loses her temper. 2 He shouted at my mother. 3 She explained things clearly. 4 He punished children who behaved badly. 5 She is friendly and she smiles a lot. 6 She asked difficult questions.

Grammar: *used to/would*
3 *When I was a child …*
1 I used to/would spend my holidays with my grandparents. 2 My grandmother would/used to cook delicious meals. 3 She used to keep chickens, goats and horses. 4 My cousin and I used to/would ride the horses every day. 5 My favourite horse was called Racer. 6 Racer used to be faster than all the other horses. 7 I didn't use to understand how dangerous riding could be. 8 One day I fell off Racer and broke my arm. 9 My mother didn't/wouldn't let me ride him again. 10 After that, I used to/would sit in the house and watch sadly as the horses played in the field.

4a 1 I used to play volleyball when I was at school. 2 Did Sylvie use to smoke? 3 When I was younger, I didn't use to like mushrooms. 4 I used to enjoy cooking a lot. Now I don't have enough time. 5 She used to drink milk when she was a child but now she is allergic to it. 6 He didn't use to play computer games. Now he is always playing them. 7 I used to read a lot of books when I was at university. I don't read so many now. 8 Did you use to study at the Anglo–American school?

b Sentences 1, 4, 5, 7

Listening: childhood
5 1 No, he didn't. 2 The art of keeping still. 3 No. 4 No, she said he was 'less trouble than he used to be'.

6 1 T 2 F 3 F 4 F 5 T 6 F 7 F 8 F 9 T 10 T

Pronunciation: silent letters
7a 1 I thou**gh**t to myself 2 my mother wou**l**d mention 3 she was ta**l**king 4 the nau**gh**ty children 5 less trouble than he use**d** to be

c

silent *gh*	silent *l*	silent *w*	silent *d*	silent *k*
thought	walk	saw	used to	knew
bought	talk	knew		knee
taught	should			
naughty	would			

Lesson 7.3
Vocabulary: old age
1 1 retire 2 respected 3 elderly 4 senior citizens 5 nursing homes 6 pensions

Grammar: past ability
2 1 could paint 2 was able to tell 3 managed to write 4 was able to read 5 managed to publish 6 could play

3 1 I didn't manage to pass my driving test until I was thirty. 2 Tim wasn't able to swim at school because of his ear infections. 3 We were sitting near the back of the concert hall but we could hear the music beautifully. 4 Were you able to see the actors without wearing your glasses? 5 I played rugby at school, but I never managed to get into the team. 6 We couldn't walk to school as children because it was too far. 7 Abigail was able to read music when she was only four years old. 8 Boris wasn't able to join the choir because his voice was too quiet. 9 He managed to learn the music off by heart. 10 Susan wasn't able to sing because she had a sore throat.

Reading
4 Title 3 is best: Not the retiring type

5 56 years: the number of years Dorothy Beckett has worked in the cake factory. 9.30: the time Gerald Lilley arrives in the office when he isn't travelling. 70: many of the other workers are 70 years younger than Dorothy Beckett. 4 million: the annual turnover for the cake business. 40 hours: the number of hours Dorothy Beckett works a week. 72: the number of years ago that William Spencer started work as a car salesman. 1945: the year that Dorothy Beckett started the factory with her husband, Fred. 94: Mr Lilley is 94 years old. 90s: all the people in the article are in their 90s.

6 1 Three things that people can do when they stop working are gardening, taking holidays and chatting with friends. 2 Her work involves putting cakes in boxes. 3 Some are 22 years old. 4 No. 5 No, he wanted to be a lawyer. 6 He didn't have the right qualifications. 7 He is paid for his experience. 8 He works from 9.30a.m. to 4.00p.m. 9 He lives in New York. 10 Long flights 11 He enjoys reading poetry to relax.

Review and consolidation unit 7

Vocabulary
1 **Across** 2 graduated 5 mistake 7 course 8 failed
Down 1 progress 3 revised 4 research 5 marks 6 notes

Subject/object questions
2 1 Who went to the meeting? 2 ✓ 3 What happened? 4 Where was Shakespeare born? 5 Who wrote Macbeth? 6 ✓ 7 Who telephoned the engineer? 8 ✓ 9 ✓ 10 Who ate the cake?

Vocabulary
3 1 fast learner 2 strict 3 practice/perfect 4 steep/curve 5 heart 6 picked 7 thrown/deep 8 brought

Adjectives in descriptions/professional qualities
4 1 pale 2 slim 3 fragile 4 mild 5 fierce 6 gigantic 7 open-minded 8 knowledgeable 9 loses his temper 10 understanding

Used to/would/ Past Simple
5 1 B 2 C 3 B/C 4 A/B 5 A 6 C 7 A/C 8 B

6 1 retire 2 pension 3 senior citizen 4 nursing home 5 respect/elderly

Ability: past and present

7 1 managed 2 couldn't 3 able to 4 manage to 5 couldn't
6 manage to 7 wasn't able to 8 couldn't 9 could 10 weren't able to

Vocabulary

8 1 have 2 gave 3 wild 4 up 5 teacher's 6 bookworm
7 brush 8 out 9 learn 10 colours

Unit 8 Change

Lesson 8.1
Vocabulary: phrases with *change*

1 1 changed career 2 changed the subject 3 change of heart
4 changed my mind 5 make a change 6 time for a change

Reading and vocabulary: the law

2 1 illegal 2 arrested 3 offence 4 forbidden 5 fine

3 1 A London taxi. 2 If he needed to use the toilet. 3 They can be arrested. 4 Yes, but you must not wake the bears. 5 You might get a fine. 6 You should be careful not to have a particular haircut (a bob).

4 A: It is illegal to enter the Houses of Parliament wearing a suit of armour.
B: In Alaska, it is an offence to push a moose out of an aeroplane.
C: In Florida, you cannot tie an elephant to a parking meter.
D: In London, taxis have to carry hay and oats for their horses.

Grammar: second conditional

5 1 d 2 f 3 e 4 a 5 h 6 g 7 b 8 c

6 1 found/would you pick 2 gave/would you tell 3 Would you smoke/could 4 Would/throw/fined 5 thought/would you drive
6 Would/played 7 heard/would you try

7 1 'll 2 wanted 3 wouldn't 4 didn't 5 stops 6 had
7 would 8 asked 9 would 10 won't

Lesson 8.2
Vocabulary: global issues

1 1 lifestyle 2 crime 3 cure 4 problems/developing/war
5 starvation 6 environment 7 security 8 standard/developed
9 pollution 10 disease

Grammar: adverbs

2 1 I couldn't understand her because she was talking too *quickly*.
2 Be *careful* when you turn the light on! The switch is broken. 3 ✓
4 I *definitely* don't want to be late. 5 We will *possibly* see her at the theatre. 6 ✓ 7 *Hopefully* she'll call us tomorrow. 8 ✓
9 I couldn't see the film *clearly* because I didn't have my glasses.
10 ✓

3 1 loudly 2 unfortunately 3 personally 4 probably
5 completely 6 clearly 7 really/beautifully 8 basically

How to …

4 1 deteriorated 2 still 3 got 4 worse 5 surprisingly
6 more 7 unfortunately 8 changes

5 1 He went to Uganda. 2 He was a doctor. 3 Yes, he did.

6 1b 2c 3f 4a 5e 6g 7d

7 1 volunteer 2 the bush 3 homesick 4 contribute 5 priest
6 banks 7 resources 8 expertise

Lesson 8.3
Vocabulary: life decisions

1 1 decided 2 went 3 left 4 buy 5 have 6 given up
7 retire 8 start

Grammar: third conditional

2 1 B 2 A 3 C 4 B 5 A 6 C 7 B 8 C

3 1 If there hadn't been so much traffic, she would have caught the plane. 2 If the suit hadn't been reduced, the man wouldn't have been able to buy it. 3 If there hadn't been water on the floor, the waiter wouldn't have slipped. 4 They wouldn't have got so wet if they'd had umbrellas. 5 If they had known it would be so busy, they would have booked a table. 6 If he had known she had a boyfriend already, he wouldn't have asked her out to dinner.

Listening

4

	What was the decision about?	What was the situation before?	What was the situation afterwards?	Why did they make the decision?	Are they happy with the decision they made?
Rachel	what to study at university/ her career	she was studying medicine	she studied psychology	she didn't enjoy lectures/ found working in the hospital environment difficult	yes
Justin	to start a family	worked hard/ travelled/ went out a lot and enjoyed freedom	met Shan/ got married/ had children/ doesn't work late or travel/stays at home to baby-sit in the evenings	He met Shan, lived together, and his priorities started to change	yes

5 1 Rachel 2 Justin 3 Rachel 4 Justin 5 Rachel 6 Justin

6 1 F 2 F 3 T 4 F 5 T 6 T 7 F 8 F

Review and consolidation unit 8

Expressions with *change*

1a change the subject   change my clothes   makes a change
change my career   change the password   time for a change
change her hairstyle   change of heart

b 1 change my career. 2 changed her hairstyle. 3 change the subject. 4 changed the password. 5 makes a change. 6 change of heart. 7 change my clothes. 8 time for a change.

First and second conditionals

2 1 wait 2 wouldn't 3 went 4 go 5 gave 6 'll call
7 wanted 8 won 9 won't 10 don't start

Cause and result

3 1 mean 2 result 3 lead 4 means 5 caused 6 because
7 so 8 Therefore

Global issues

4 *Corrected sentences:* 1 Starvation is a terrible problem in some developing countries. 2 Luckily, they have found a cure for this awful disease. (Or '... cures for these awful diseases'.) 3 I think my standard of living has improved since I came to this country.
4 I don't like the city because there is too much pollution.
5 I think countries should stop having wars. They need to make peace. 6 The lifestyles of the rich and famous must be very difficult.
7 There are a lot of crimes in this part of the city. 8 We must find a solution to the problem. 9 Now we can contact people in other countries very easily with the Internet. 10 People all over the world have mobile phones.

How to …

5a and b 1 situation ✓ 2 better ✓ 3 still/same ✗
4 deteriorated ✓ 5 less ✓ 6 surprisingly/changed ✗

Adverbs

6 1 A 2 B 3 C 4 A 5 C 6 B 7 C

Third conditional

7 1 If I hadn't bought a new car, I would have had enough money to go on holiday. 2 If the manager hadn't been so difficult to work for, we wouldn't have left the company. 3 The job would have been finished on time if the builders hadn't taken long lunch breaks.
4 We wouldn't have sat in the garden eating ice creams if it hadn't been a sunny day. 5 If she hadn't fallen and broken her leg, she would have become a professional dancer. 6 He wouldn't have arrived late for work if the train hadn't been delayed. 7 I wouldn't have signed the contract if I had read it carefully. 8 Picasso might not have painted such beautiful landscapes if he hadn't lived by the sea. 9 She wouldn't have felt so lonely if she hadn't lived by herself. 10 If John Lennon hadn't been a famous rock star, his son might/would not have become a well-known musician.

Vocabulary

8 1 dishonest **2** undercooked **3** government **4** treatment
5 accommodation **6** importance **7** unemployment
8 independence **9** movement **10** difference

Unit 9 Jobs

Lesson 9.1
Vocabulary: work

1 1 qualifications **2** challenges **3** experienced **4** promoted
5 perks **6** long hours **7** overtime **8** pay rise **9** references
10 rewarding

Grammar: *make, let, allow*

2 1 Our boss doesn't let us smoke in the office. **2** Employees
are allowed to wear jeans to work. **3** The new manager makes
us work very hard. **4** Most children are not allowed to watch TV
after 10p.m. **5** The teacher let us use our dictionaries. **6** Ruby
makes her son make his bed. **7** Children are not allowed in the
club. **8** The restaurant owner didn't let my dog into the restaurant/
let me take my dog into the restaurant.

3 1 makes **2** allowed **3** doesn't let **4** make **5** allowed to
6 let

4 1 Good afternoon **2** Firstly, I'm going to talk about **3** I'd like to
tell you **4** Secondly, I'll talk about **5** Our main idea **6** The most
important thing for us is **7** In conclusion, **8** Thank you **9** Are
there any questions

Listening

5 b

6 1 an employer **2** what they want **3** less/later **4** a few
years ago/increased **5** relaxed/more/later **6** better **7** do
8 occasionally **9** decide for themselves **10** politicians and
businessmen/formal

Lesson 9.2
Vocabulary: -*ing*/-*ed* adjectives

1 1 frightening **2** excited **3** depressing **4** bored
5 relaxing **6** exhausted **7** confusing **8** annoyed **9** tiring
10 frightened

Grammar: reported speech

2 1 said **2** asked **3** told **4** asked **5** said **6** told **7** asked
8 told **9** ask **10** say **11** told **12** asked **13** ask **14** told/said

3 1 She said that her name was Josie and she came from Brazil.
2 She said that she was living in London, and (was) working in a café.
3 She said that she had been there (here) for three months and she
really liked it, but she missed her family and friends too. **4** She said
that she wanted to go back home at Christmas, but she didn't earn
very much money, so she couldn't afford the flight. **5** She said that
she had phoned her brother the day before, and that he was going to
visit her the following month. **6** She said that maybe she would ask
him to lend her some money. **7** She said that when she went back
to Brazil, she would never forget her experiences in England.
8 She said that she had made a lot of great friends.

Reading

4 1 – paragraph 4 **2** – paragraph 2 **3** – Introduction
4 – paragraph 1 **5** – paragraph 5 **6** – paragraph 3

5 1 lose your temper, go crazy **2** poor management **3** deal with
4 a management technique **5** respect **6** bully **7** work out
8 calm down **9** slow down

6 The article describes how *poor* management is the main reason
why people *lose* their *tempers* at work, and it offers advice to help
workers *deal* with a difficult boss. It explains how some managers
use anger as a management *technique* in order to make employees
respect them. Some bosses may *bully* new staff to see how they
react. It is important to *work* out why your boss is angry, so that you
can try to avoid it. If this doesn't work, and your boss goes *crazy*, the
article suggests that you take deep breaths to help slow *down* your
breathing, and this will help you to *calm* down.

Lesson 9.3
Grammar: past obligation/permission

1 1 We were allowed to smoke at my school. **2** In my last job
we could ask the computer engineer to help if we had problems.
3 I didn't have to pay the extra money in the end. **4** Were
you allowed to go to parties when you were younger? **5** They
had to wait for three hours before they were allowed into the
exhibition. **6** I couldn't use my mobile phone because I was
in the library. **7** Did you have to wait a long time to get a refund?
8 We had to leave our suitcases at the airport so that they could
be checked. **9** You aren't allowed to wear shoes in here. **10** In
my last school, we weren't allowed to use the Internet for more than
twenty minutes.

2 line 1: ✓ line 2: to line 3: had line 4: ✓ line 5: to
line 6: allowed line 7: ✓ line 8: were line 9: could line
10: couldn't line 11: have

3 1 type **2** speak **3** work well **4** give **5** use **6** dealing
7 making **8** organising **9** prioritising **10** persuading

4 The best sentence is 3.

5 1 d **2** f **3** b **4** a **5** e **6** c

6a 1 c **2** a **3** e **4** b **5** d

b 1 take one step at a time **2** get in the way **3** set a goal
4 make your dreams come true

Review and consolidation unit 9

Vocabulary: jobs

1 1 applied **2** unemployed **3** flexitime **4** challenges
5 long hours/pay rise **6** experienced **7** applying/reference
8 promoted **9** perks

make, let, allow

2 1 We *are* not allowed to go into the conference hall. **2** She
wouldn't let me *to* see a doctor. **3** They should *to* make her get
a job. **4** Did they make you fill*ing* in a form? **5** Am I allow*ed* to
smoke? **6** The landlord doesn't *to* let us have parties. **7** Her
parents let *to* her *to* do anything she wants. **8** He's angry because
we won't let *him* go to the cinema alone. **9** Why *aren't* we allowed
to speak during the test? **10** When we play chess together, my
father always *lets me* win.

How to ...

3 1 I'd like to tell you about ... **2** Firstly, I'm going to talk about ...
3 The most important thing for us is ... **4** Our main idea is ...
5 Secondly, I'll talk about ... **6** To sum up ...

Vocabulary

4 1 tired/relaxing **2** frightened **3** excited **4** annoying
5 confusing **6** depressed **7** exhausted **8** boring **9** rewarded
10 interesting

Reported speech

5 1 asked **2** told/asked **3** asked **4** tell/ask **5** asked, said
6 said **7** asked **8** said **9** asked, told **10** said
6 1 B **2** C **3** C **4** A **5** C **6** B

Past obligation/permission

7 1 had to **2** didn't have to **3** weren't allowed **4** could
5 wasn't allowed **6** had to **7** couldn't **8** didn't have to

Job requirements

8 1 presentations **2** long/irregular **3** solving **4** accurately
5 range **6** figures **7** delegating **8** prioritise **9** decisions
10 pressure

Vocabulary

9 1 posted **2** movie **3** flat **4** high school **5** soccer **6** toilet
7 mall **8** petrol **9** mobile phone **10** main road/motorway
11 pavement **12** elevator

Unit 10 Memories

Lesson 10.1
Vocabulary: verbs connected with memory
1 **1** remember **2** miss **3** reminds **4** forgetting **5** remind me to **6** lost **7** remember **8** reminds me of **9** miss **10** forgotten

Grammar: *wish/if only*
2 **1** we had **2** I could afford **3** she hadn't missed **4** you wouldn't **5** we hadn't been **6** you lived **7** wish I was **8** I spoke *or* I could speak **9** I hadn't eaten **10** you would

3 **A** I wish I could run faster.
B I wish I had more money.
C I wish I had revised.
D I wish I hadn't gone skiing.
E I wish I wasn't so short.
F I wish I hadn't bought this car.

Vocabulary: nature collocations
4 **1**C **2**B **3**A **4**C **5**A

Reading
5a **C** Improves your memory

b **1** Because they have to function with just a few hours' sleep. **2** The people who suffer from Alzheimer's Disease. **3** To find a pill that increases the memory. **4** Would it be used only by ill people, or by people who wanted an advantage in life (eg lazy, rich students)? **5** Start asking their workers to take pills so that they performed better. **6** It was originally for injured soldiers. Now it's used by 'middle-aged actors who want to stay prettier for longer'. **7** A few more years, probably. **8** He says, 'It isn't clear that animals use the same kind of memories as humans'.

c **a** paragraph 5 **b** paragraph 4 **c** paragraph 1 **d** paragraph 2 **e** paragraph 3

d **1** exams **2** work **3** sleep **4** questions **5** tested

Lesson 10.2
Vocabulary: describing great people
1 **1** determined **2** talented **3** dedicated **4** courage **5** involved **6** encouraged

Grammar: past tenses review
2 **1** had already been **2** was walking **3** wrote **4** had already started **5** had been

3 **1** had known **2** had broken down **3** were you talking **4** had switched on **5** were waiting **6** was listening **7** had never been

4 **1** was travelling **2** had already suffered **3** painted **4** was attending **5** was working **6** had finished **7** went **8** were staying **9** had got **10** were waiting **11** talked **12** had become

How to ...
5 **1** ✓ **2** one million **3** the nineteen seventies **4** ✓ **5** one thousand two hundred and ninety-eight **6** three quarters **7** ✓ **8** ninety-nine point nine percent **9** ✓ **10** ✓ **11** nineteen sixty-nine **12** eleven and a half

6a **1** 16,349 **2** $\frac{1}{3}$ **3** 14% **4** 3rd December 2006/03.12.06 **5** $88.71 **6** 1970s

b **1** twenty-three thousand, nine hundred and ninety-three pounds **2** three quarters **3** ninety-nine point eight percent **4** the nineteen-nineties **5** the thirtieth of December, two thousand and seven **6** the twentieth century

c **1** A 4,998 **2** B £79.99 **3** B 50% **4** B 15/11/03 **5** A 6½ **6** B 1980s **6** 6½ **7** A 21st century **8** B 10th July 1969 **9** B 1,000,000 **10** B $1,345

Lesson 10.3
Grammar: phrasal verbs
1 **1** up **2** through **3** on **4** off **5** up **6** up **7** up **8** on **9** back **10** out

2 **1** split up **2** will call off **3** put up with **4** was going on **5** will carry on **6** turn up **7** isn't coming back **8** found out **9** is going through **10** come up with

Writing: formal vs informal
3a **1** j **2** i **3** k **4** f **5** b **6** e **7** d **8** h **9** a **10** c **11** g

b **1** Thanks a lot **2** I can come **3** I'll be there at 8.30 **4** Best wishes **5** You're welcome **6** You can get more info on the website **7** I'll get in touch **8** See you soon

Listening
4a Individual answers

b **1** Review new words regularly (almost every day). ⬚5 **2** Stick notes around your house with new words on them. ⬚1 **3** Test yourself regularly. ⬚2 **4** Use new words in class whenever you can. ⬚6 **5** Draw pictures of words and phrases. ⬚4 **6** Read your notes before you go to bed. ⬚3

c **1** A **2** C **3** A **4** C **5** B **6** B

Review and consolidation unit 10

wish/if only
1 **1** A **2** C **3** B **4** A **5** C **6** B **7** A **8** C

wish/if only and past tenses
2 **1** never been to/not been to **2** could stop smoking **3** had cleaned the room **4** was working **5** hadn't thrown away **6** I was **7** had already met **8** was eating

3 **1** had already bought **2** was watching **3** didn't go **4** was dancing **5** had left **6** put **7** was trying **8** hadn't seen **9** had taken **10** wasn't staying

Phrasal verbs
4 **1** We called off the picnic because it was raining. **2** Can you tell me what is going on? **3** You have to come up with a solution. **4** Jean always turns up late. **5** Climbers can put up with cold weather. **6** I'll find out what happened last night. **7** They're going through a difficult period. **8** When are you planning to come back? **9** They've split up several times before. **10** Carry on running for as long as possible.

5 **1** is going on **2** haven't found out **3** carry on **4** are going through **5** comes back **6** turned up **7** had split up **8** put up with **9** come up with **10** call off

Vocabulary: personal qualities
6 **1** involved **2** inspired **3** talented **4** brave **5** determined **6** dedicated **7** encourages **8** brilliant

Vocabulary: memory and the senses
7 **1** B **2** B **3** C **4** A **5** B **6** B **7** C **8** A **9** C **10** A

Writing: thank you letters
8 **1** Thanks a lot *for* letting me stay. **2** *Best* wishes, **3** We *look* forward to working with you. **4** I am writing *to* thank you for all your hard work. **5** Thank you for *helping* me last weekend. **6** I *had* a great time. **7** I hope to see you *soon*. **8** Your efforts *were* appreciated.

Pearson Education Limited,
Edinburgh Gate, Harlow
Essex, CM20 2JE, England
and Associated Companies throughout the world
www.longman.com

The right of Antonia Clare and JJ Wilson to be identified as authors of
this work has been asserted by them in accordance with the Copyright,
Designs and Patents Act 1988.

First published 2006

Set in 10.5/13pt Meta Plus book and 10/13pt Meta Plus Normal

Printed in Spain by Mateu Cromo, S.A. Pinto (Madrid)

ISBN-13: 978-1-4058-2245-9 (Workbook only with key)
ISBN-10: 1-4058-2245-7
ISBN-13: 978-0-582-84188-8 (Workbook only without key)
ISBN-10: 0-582-84188-7
ISBN-13: 978-0-582-84187-1 (Workbook with key for pack)
ISBN-10: 1-582-84187-9
ISBN-13: 978-1-4058-2652-5 (Workbook without key for pack)
ISBN-10: 1-4058-2652-5
ISBN-13: 978-1-4058-2260-2 (Workbook with key and CD-ROM pack)
ISBN-10: 1-4058-2260-0
ISBN-13: 978-1-4058-2692-1 (Workbook without key and CD-ROM pack)
ISBN-10: 1-4058-2692-4

Illustrated by: John Batten, Chris Pavely, Roger Wade-Walker

Photo Acknowledgements
We are grateful to the following for permission to reproduce photographs:
Alamy: pg52 (Purestock); **Ardea:** pg54; **Corbis:** pg7, pg15(m), pg63, pg65(b), pg78; **Empics:** pg9, pg15(t), pg38; **Getty
Images:** pg56(l & r), pg65(t), pg70; **Kirsten Holt:** pg45(b); **Frank Lane Picture Library:** pg47(br); **Lonely Planet Images:**
pg47(bl); **Punchstock:** pg57(tl & r) (Corbis), pg57(bl) (Creatas); **Rex Features:** pg15(b), pg33; **Sally & Richard Greenhill:**
pg10; **Science Photo Library:** pg77; **Sinopix:** pg5; **South American Pictures:** pg45(t & m); **The Travel Library:** pg74(t).

Cover images by Getty Images (t), Lonely Planet images (left), Punchstock / Bananastock (b).

Picture research by Kevin Brown

Every effort has been made to trace the copyright holders and we apologise in advance for any unintentional omissions.
We would be pleased to insert the appropriate acknowledgement in any subsequent edition of this publication.